TRAINING LACTATE PULSE RATE

D0453991

Peter G.J.M. Janssen

photos
Soenar Chamid
Duursport Actueel
Cor Eberhard
Marjan Janssen
Focus on the Marathon
Pierre van de Meulenhof
Steven E. Sutton
The Star, Malaysia
Wout Steensma
Fer Traugott
Helmuth Vonk
Cor Vos
Pienie Zwitserlood

ISBN 952-90066-8-3
Printed in Oy Liitto 1989 Oulu Finland
Publisher: Polar Electro Oy
© 1987 Peter G.J.M. Janssen

Translation: Hans Strijbosch, Stiphout
Preparatory typesetting: Rianne Coolen, Helenaveen

cover and layout: Tom Küsters, Groesbeek

TRAINING
LACTATE
PULSE RATE

Tim Malloy

To:
Marjan, Steven, Barbara, Krijn, Merel
Deurne, January 1989

CONTENTS

PREFACE

With the epidemic rise of chemically-aided training, too few coaches, and perhaps even fewer athletes, believe that the capacity for unsurpassed athletic excellence lies **within** the human body, and not in a syringe or bottle **outside** it. A small number of us work fervently in the hope that sport science can offer the coach and athlete non-chemical means to superior performance that will forever banish ergogenic aids from the athletic arena.

It is with this lofty and, I think, not unrealistic line of thinking that I introduce here a work of major magnitude by Dutch sport scientist Peter G.J.M. Janssen. As a former athlete and coach, I am pleased to immediately recognize the real-world value of Janssen's work. I wonder – wistfully – where he was when my swimming teammates and I so boldly violated all the rules that in retrospect seem so obvious. I suppose we can be forgiven, since James E. 'Doc' Counsilman's seminal work **The Science of Swimming** had only just been published (1968), and was greeted by many coaches with the traditional American to coaching response: 'Sure, sounds good. But I'm going to train you just like my coach trained me.'

Janssen brings to us one very simple key to unfailingly-accurate athletic training strategy – heart rate monitoring. As everyone who has ever competed will appreciate, the human body's cyclical highs and lows can wreak havoc with pre-planned training and competition strategies. A means to assess the body's exact state of readiness for both the positive stresses of proper training and for actual race pacing would be, and as Janssen demonstrates has **proven** to be invaluable.

Janssen offers us first a review of the energy systems that fuel athletic performance, then a primer on heart rate and the internal and external factors that affect it.

Next, using the research-proven ECG-accurate wireless heart rate monitoring technology developed and commercially-implemented by Polar Electro Oy of Finland, he presents a wealth of data on the relationship between heart rate, velocity of movement (runners, cyclists, and swimmers will be most at home with this work), and the correlated levels of blood lactate. Drawing heavily on the work of Italian sport scientist F. Conconi, Janssen describes the extensive work that has been done on training, heart rate, and lactate levels. Of critical importance to the book is Janssen's exposition of the concept of the 'anaerobic threshold', the point of training or competitive intensity at which the aerobic energy system can no longer provide for the body's energy needs, leading to a rise in anaerobic processing and the concomitant rise in lactic acid. It is this well-established physiological phenomenon that lies at the heart of most failures of training to hone an athlete to competitive perfection, and of athletes to perform up to expectations in a race situation. Too many athletes (present company quite sorrowfully included) have believed that more is better, that mega-miles of early-season training followed by weeks or months of sprints-to-exhaustion, that going out early in the lead and gutting it out to try to win are the keys to success. Janssen persuasively shows through actual reportage of heart-rate registrations (a feature of the high-end Polar wireless monitors) during training bouts, races, and entire seasons, that it is not **how hard** or **how much** one trains, but **the accuracy of workout or racing intensity** – as measured by the near-perfect window of heart rate response – that determines athletic success. Anyone can train hard and long, or bolt madly to the front of the pack. It is the **wise** athlete who trains, and races, right.

Towards this end, Janssen presents actual test protocols that will allow athletes in several sports to establish their own heart rate at the anaerobic threshold via nothing more than accurate heart rate monitoring, then base their training and actual races on moment-to-moment heart rate response to the rigors of physical work. Armed with this knowledge, athletes and coaches who follow the sport-specific training programs presented at the close of the book will prove to themselves once and for all that it is the **quality**, and not quantity, of training that makes a winner.

A surprising number of European athletes, Eastern Bloc as well as Western, – convinced of the power of heart rate measurement – treat their monitor as an integral part of their equipment complement. This book should open a significant number of American eyes, and perhaps prove that the key to athletic excellence lies within us, and is accessible to all.

Michael D. Wolf, Ph.D.
New York City
June 20, 1989

INTRODUCTION

Muscles during activity, or in other words during exercise, need energy for their functioning. This energy may be supplied by a number of different systems. These systems each have certain specific characteristics.

It is of great importance to know the various systems and to train them separately if required. It is possible to feel in one's own body which system is especially stressed to supply the working muscles with energy. From everyday practice it appears that many athletes do not feel very well which system they are training. In other words, they are just making a mess of things. Many of them train too intensively and others on the other hand are doing their workouts with too little intensity.

Through lactate determinations and pulse rate registrations the correct training intensities can be established. Now the maximally attainable individual levels of performance may be reached – often with less training.

ENERGY SUPPLY

The various energy-supplying systems and their characteristics

Within the body there is a chemical substance which enables muscles to contract or relax. This substance is called adenosine triphosphate, or ATP. It is a compound which, during muscular activity, transfers to adenosine diphosphate, or ADP, while producing direct energy for the muscle.
Schematically this may be presented as follows:

ATP → ADP + energy.

However, the quantity of ATP in the muscles is limited and if nothing would happen, this source of energy would soon be exhausted.
Fortunately there are a number of aiding systems in the muscle which constantly re-form ATP from the ADP already present, so that the quantity of ATP remains sufficient for the muscle to keep on the activity.
The first aiding system to be mentioned here is that of the creatine phosphate. Creatine phosphate is a substance, also present in only small quantities, which is capable of re-forming ADP into ATP very fast.
Schematically:

Creatine phosphate + ADP → creatine + ATP.

It will be clear that also this aiding system cannot offer a lasting solution. After a very short period of time practically all creatine phosphate present will be transferred into creatine. Energy supply from this source is no longer possible then. In illustration: the quantity of ATP directly available is sufficient for about 1 or 2 seconds of maximum activity, and the quantity of creatine phosphate is exhausted after about 6 to 8 seconds.

A lasting, not time-restricted solution is offered by aiding systems that burn up foodstuffs.
By burning up is meant: the oxidation of foodstuffs, mainly carbohydrates and fats. These substances are taken in together with the other nutrients and they are stored in depots to be used when needed. The store of fats, seen as an energy supply, is practically unlimited. This does not apply to the carbohydrates, i.e., sugars, starches and glucose. These are stored as glycogen, mainly in the liver and muscles. The quantity stored may vary widely but mostly it is sufficient for at least one hour of maximum exertion.

The burning up of fats is presented schematically as follows:

fats + oxygen + ADP → carbon dioxide + ATP + water.

The carbon dioxide thus formed is breathed out through the lungs then. Burning up carbohydrates is somewhat more complicated; two successive reactions are, schematically:
1st phase: glucose + ADP → lactate + ATP.
2nd phase: lactate + oxygen + ADP → carbon dioxide + ATP + water.
The first phase does not use oxygen, whereas the second does.
The lactate (also called lactic acid) formed as an intermediate product at light excercises is directly transformed in the second phase so that the eventual result is:

glucose + oxygen + ADP → carbon dioxide + ATP + water.

When the level of exertion is heightened, however, there is a point when this approach does not apply any more. The demand for energy is then such that the second phase is 'overtaxed'; its capacity is no longer sufficient to transform all

11

the lactic acid emitted in the first phase. The result is an accumulation of lactate in the working muscles. Characteristics of an accumulating acidosis are painful legs (for cyclists or runners) or painful arms (for rowers). This causes a feeling of powerlessness. The exertion cannot be maintained at the same level. Whenever a cyclist or runner must allow a gap between him and the lead, acidosis is most likely to be the cause. The athlete who can put off the moment of acidosis longest will often be the best and winner of the race.

From the muscles, lactate is transmitted to the blood circulation. From blood samples, taken during exertion, the lactic content can be established; this is mostly done in a laboratory. The lactate values thus obtained give a good impression in what way and with what intensity sports are performed. Energy production going together with high lactate values is no more than an emergency solution.

The acidosis, which is distinctly noticed by the athlete, may have considerable disadvantages. We shall discuss that later.

Summing up, you could draw up the following survey:

a. Creatine phosphate + ADP → creatine + ATP
   anaerobic, alactic.
b. Glucose + ADP → lactate + ATP (glycolysis)
   anaerobic, lactic.
c. Glucose + oxygen + ADP → water + carbon dioxide + ATP
   aerobic, alactic.
d. Fat + oxygen + ADP → water + carbon dioxide + ATP
   aerobic, alactic.

Aerobic   : using oxygen
Anaerobic : without using oxygen
Lactic   : forming lactate
Alactic   : without forming lactate.

Some characteristics of these systems:

a. The creatine phosphate system, or CP system.
The energy supplied by this system is directly available. When stressed to the maximum, this system can supply energy for about 6 to 8 seconds. The quantity of creatine phosphate is soon exhausted. Energy supply by transforming creatine phosphate takes place at the beginning of any exertion. The rebuild-up of CP after finishing the exertion is also fast. After 22 seconds about half the quantity of CP and after some 44 seconds three-quarters has been restored. The CP system is trained by power bursts alternated with periods of rest. The period of rest should by long enough since the rebuild-up of CP costs time.

b. A kind of emergency system that springs into action when a level of exertion is surpassed which varies from individual to individual. Depending on the degree of surpassing and conditioning of the person in question, it leads to the necessity of stopping the exertion within a period of some seconds to some minutes.

After breaking off the exertion it may be for some 20 to 30 minutes before all the lactate present in the body is neutralized; high lactate concentrations give a feeling of fatigue, thick legs and painful muscles. Furthermore it causes heavy breathing and a tendency to stop the exertion.

c. and d. The aerobic energy supply needs some time to be well activated (2 or 3 minutes). The store of carbohydrates is limited; practically speaking, the store of fats is unlimited. The two systems work simultaneously, it is true, but their share in the total process of energy supply varies; moreover, it depends on the level of exertion and conditioning.

With long-lasting submaximal performances the carbohydrate fuel system is dominant at first, but bit by bit its leading role is taken over by the burning up of fats. In this way the body protects its remaining glycogen depots.

The combined aerobic system is excellent and it can be trained till old age. Improvements of capacity by a factor of 50 have been recorded.

Schematic survey:

Classification of maximum activity of various duration together with energy-supplying system for this activity			
duration	classification (aerobic/anaerobic)	energy supplied by	observations
1-4 sec.	anaerobic, alactic	ATP	
4-20 sec.	anaerobic, alactic	ATP + CP	
20-45 sec.	anaerobic, alactic + anaerobic, lactic	ATP + CP + muscle glycogen	high lactate production
45-120 sec.	anaerobic, lactic	muscle glycogen	with increasing duration, decreasing lactate production
120-140 sec.	aerobic + anaerobic, lactic	muscle glycogen	ditto
240-600 sec.	aerobic	muscle glycogen + fatty acids	with increasing duration higher share of fats
etc.			

Various substrates for energy supply and their characteristics			
substrate	breakdown	availability	speed of energy production
creatine phosphate (CP)	anaerobic, alactic	very limited	very fast
glycogen or glucose	anaerobic, lactic	limited	fast
glucose or glycogen	aerobic, alactic	limited	slow
fatty acids	aerobic, alactic	unlimited	sluggish

energy supply	anaerobic, alactic	anaerobic, lactic	aerobic, alactic
energy via	ATP/CP	glycolysis	burning with oxygen
yields	direct energy	2-3 mM ATP	36 mM ATP
time	15 sec.	15 sec. - 2 or 3 min.	longer than 2-3 min.
by-product	no lactate	lactate	no lactate
name	phosphate battery	lactic system	aerobic system
activity	start of exertion, sprint	breakaway, brief exertion	long-lasting exertion
examples	100-meter sprint	closing a gap, 1 km cycling time trial, 400-800 meters running	endurance cycling, marathon, long distances
capacity	sprinting capacity	lactate tolerance capacity	endurance capacity

CARBOHYDRATES, FATS AND PROTEINS AS SOURCES OF ENERGY

The most important source of energy for performing intensively in sports is carbohydrates. Carbohydrates are capable of supplying most energy per time unit. Whenever the intensity of the exertion is lower, the burning of fat begins to play an important role.

A 400-meter runner gets his energy supplied via the burning up of carbohydrates. For a cyclist or marathon runner, sports in which endurance is most important, the burning up of fat is used. The cyclist in the final part of the race or during a breakaway will have to switch over to carbohydrates because fats supply insufficient energy. Team tactics as seen in cycling are virtually based on this principle. Every team has a captain or 'protected rider' and several domestiques, as they are called. The domestiques keep their captain free from the wind, enabling him to begin fresh at the final part of the race. The domestiques are burning up carbohydrates and by the end of the race they are burnt-out completely. The captain however, is pedaling along in the shelter of his lieutenants. His exertion is less intense, which enables him to save his carbohydrates for the final.

For well-trained persons the quantity of carbohydrates is a bout 700-800 gm. This quantity is sufficient to last for 60-90 minutes of intense exertion.
When, during these 60 to 90 minutes carbohydrates are not replenished, a low glucose content of the blood will arise. This is the moment of 'the man with the hammer' or 'getting the bonks'. The fats and proteins become, when glycogen depots are exhausted, the most important sources of energy. This shift is irrevocably accompanied by a drop of speed.

Some observations can also be made about fats as a source of energy. Taken as a whole, nutrition in the western world is far too fat. Therefore the intake of

15

fats should be limited. Fat reserves for most athletes are about 10 to 15 kg. Theoretically this quantity is enough for 15,000 minutes of brisk walking or 4,000 minutes of marathon running.

Joggers with obesity who want to lose weight should be advised to practice sports with a low intensity. Thus the burning up of fats is stimulated to the maximum, with loss of body weight as a result.

As has been mentioned above, intensive exertion goes together with the burning up of carbohydrates and less intensive exertion with the burning up of fats. By training it is possible to realize a shift in the direction of burning up fats. After a period of training there is an increase in the capacity of performance. A well-trained athlete is capable of performing up to 80% of his total capacity on fats as a source of energy. When he performs between 80 and 100% of his total capacity, he is burning up carbohydrates. An untrained athlete, on the other hand, cannot tax his fat-fuel system over 50% of his total capacity.

He will have to resort to carbohydrates sooner.

After this period of training a shift has taken place in the direction of burning up fats, which means that the well-trained athlete burns fats longer, thus saving his carbohydrates.

Schematically this shift can be presented as follows:

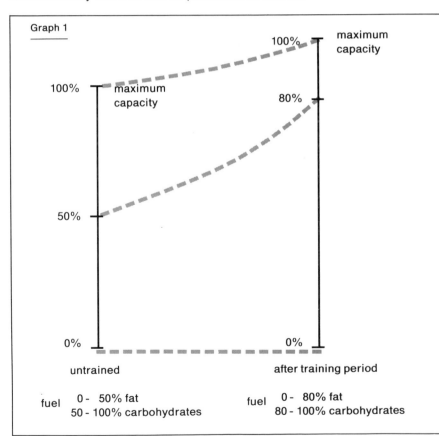

Graph 1

untrained

fuel   0 - 50% fat
50 - 100% carbohydrates

after training period

fuel   0 - 80% fat
80 - 100% carbohydrates

The last word has not been spoken about proteins as a source of energy. Up till a few years ago there was a widespread opinion that proteins did not play any role at all in the supply of energy during sports activities. Recent investigations, however, prove that proteins do play such role. For endurance sports 5 to 15% of the energy supplied comes from proteins. This percentage may even rise when some very strenuous workouts are done successively or when the duration of the exertion increases further, as in (ultra) marathons and triathlons. A large use of proteins as a source of energy is disadvantageous. The proteins that are used partly come from the muscles. The muscles are more or less 'eaten', thus influencing the performance to the negative. The recommendation that an endurance athlete can do with 0.75 to 1 gm protein/kg/day has therefore been reviewed and at present endurance athletes are said to need 1.5 to 2 gm protein/kg/day. An endurance sportsman weighing 70 kg has a daily need of 70 x 1.5 = 105 gm of protein to 70 x 2 = 140 gm of protein.

For consumption, proteins of animal origin should be preferred to vegetable proteins.

Generally animal proteins contain more essential amino acids than vegetable proteins. This means that in order to take in the complete range, less of them should be consumed. Moreover, animal proteins are digested better so that, relatively, one needs less.

Milk protein is very attractive to athletes because it contains all essential amino acids in considerable quantities and because it is easy to digest and can be concentrated.

SOME FIGURES ON THE OXIDATION OF CARBOHYDRATES, FATS AND PROTEINS

The oxidation of carbohydrates, fats and proteins supply different amounts of energy.

The oxidation of 1 gm carbohydrates supplies 17.22 kJ (4.1 cal), 1 gm fat supplies 39.6 kJ (9.4 cal) and 1 gm protein supplies 17.22 kJ.

At first sight fats seem to be the most economical fuel. Yet this is not always true as different amounts of oxygen are necessary for the oxidation of these three fuels.

When burning up carbohydrates 1 liter of oxygen supplies 21 kJ (5 cal), when burning up fats 1 liter of oxygen supplies 18.9 kJ (4.5 cal) and when proteins are burnt 1 liter of oxygen supplies 72.6 kJ (17.3 cal).

During physical exercise the body will avail itself of that fuel that can best be taken with the given intake of oxygen. Therefore when the exertion is of low intensity the body will burn fats, because oxygen intake is not restricted at that intensity, but when the exertion is more intensive, when oxygen intake is more limited, carbohydrates will be preferred. Proteins have to take a long route in the body before being available as a fuel; therefore, they are not the most economical fuel, despite their favorable fuel/oxygen/energy relation.

C.H.	oxidation: 1 gram	17.22 kJ	1 liter O_2	21 kJ.
Fat	oxidation: 1 gram	39.6 kJ	1 liter O_2	18.9 kJ.
Protein oxidation: 1 gram		17.22 kJ	1 liter O_2	72.6 kJ.

Carbohydrates (C.H.) require relatively less oxygen (O_2); therefore, intense workouts require carbohydrates.

Fats require relatively more oxygen; therefore, less intense workouts require fats.

Proteins follow a long, energy-consuming route.

PULSE RATE AND PHYSICAL EXERCISE

In everyday practice of training pulse rate is often used as a standard for the intensity of the workout. The reason for using pulse rate as a standard of exertion is the discovery that there is a linear correlation between pulse rate on the one hand and workout intensity on the other.

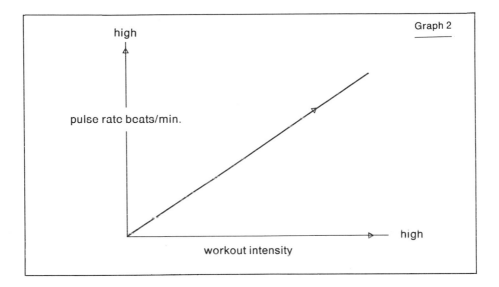

For endurance training it can be said that the best training stimulus is obtained at an intensity at which the complete oxygen-transporting system is activated to the maximum, while lactate accumulation in the muscles is not yet reached. This intensity range is also called the aerobic-anaerobic passing zone.
Many endurance workouts are done at a pulse rate (PR) of about 180 beats per minute. This intensity of training, however, seen in the light of the aerobic-anaerobic passage, is mostly too high. The aerobic-anaerobic passage may vary widely from person to person. Roughly speaking it lies within a PR range between 140 and 180 beats per minute. One athlete is training his endurance capacity best at a PR of 140; the other will have to train at a PR of 180 in order to improve his endurance capacity.

CONCONI'S PRINCIPLE

Professor Conconi advised Francesco Moser in his successful attempt to break Eddy Merckx' world-hour-record. Conconi made use of the existing correlation between activity intensity and pulse rate. He found, as other investigators had found before, that at very intensive activity pulse rate and intensity not run parallel. The straight line of the onset deflects at high intensities. In other words, the intensity may be increased but the increase of pulse rate lags at a certain point. This point is the PR deflection point. The workout intensity corresponding to this point is the maximum activity that can be done with aerobic energy supply. The deflection in the curve marks the point at what PR or what activity intensity (e.g., the speed of running or cycling) the athlete shifts from aerobic to mainly anaerobic energy supply. In this way Conconi could exactly establish the speed that Moser had to maintain without getting exhausted prematurely.

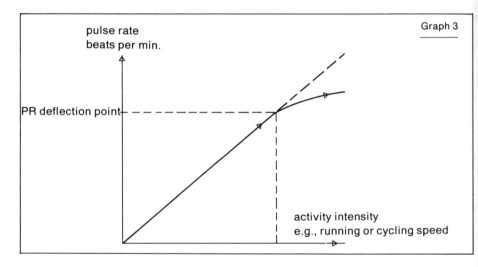

The bend marks the maximum speed that corresponds with the PR deflection point, which can be maintained during a long period of time.
It is the highest speed or PR which is supplied of energy fully aerobically. If the speed is increased, an accumulation of lactate will arise. In this situation the aerobic energy supplying system does not suffice; the anaerobic system is called upon, with the result an increasing accumulation of lactate.
A great advantage of Conconi's method is that taking blood samples is not necessary. Therefore, this method is also called the bloodless method of establishing the deflection point.

Conconi's method of working is dealt with later in more detail.

Italian pro cyclist Francesco Moser in his (first) successful attempt to break the world hour record in Mexico, Januari 1984.

THE INFLUENCE OF ENDURANCE TRAINING ON PULSE RATE

After a period of endurance training the reaction of pulse rates, at the same level of exertion, has undergone considerable changes. The example at the left shows the PR range of an untrained person. At the right, the same person after a period of endurance training.

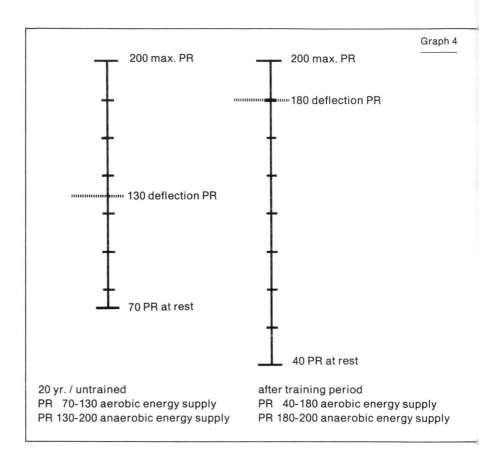

Graph 4

200 max. PR

130 deflection PR

70 PR at rest

20 yr. / untrained
PR   70-130 aerobic energy supply
PR 130-200 anaerobic energy supply

200 max. PR

180 deflection PR

40 PR at rest

after training period
PR   40-180 aerobic energy supply
PR 180-200 anaerobic energy supply

The maximum pulse rate

In the example the untrained athlete has a maximum pulse rate of 200 beats per minute. After a period of training the maximum PR remains at the same level. So whether trained or untrained the maximum PR does not depend on conditioning. In very well-trained endurance athletes a drop in maximum PR may arise.

The maximum pulse rate can only be established when the athlete has fully rested. A complete recovery after the latest workout is necessary. It is established as follows:

After a warm-up period of some 15 minutes the athlete does an all-out 5 minutes of running or cycling. The last 20 to 30 seconds are sprinted. The maximum pulse rate can now simply be read on the pulse rate meter.

Counting the pulse is also possible immediately after the exertion. Due to counting mistakes and the fast drop of pulse rate immediately after the exertion this method is less accurate.

Pulse rate at rest

For well-trained endurance athletes the pulse rate at rest is low. For untrained persons the pulse rate at rest is between 70 to 80 beats per minute. As the endurance capacity is improved, the PR at rest will gradually decrease. In well-training endurance athletes (cyclists, marathon runners) PR values at rest are counted between 40 and 50 beats per minute. Even under 40 beats per minute is sometimes seen. Women have a pulse rate at rest of about 10 beats more than men of the same age. In the morning this rate is about 10 beats less than in the same situation in the evening. This also applies for the maximum pulse rate.

Pulse rate at the deflection point

The most important change arising after a period of endurance training is a shift of the deflection point to a higher PR. In the example the untrained person has a deflection point of 130.
After a period of endurance training the deflection point moves from 130 to a PR of 180 beats per minute. An exertion with an intensity beyond the PR of the deflection point goes together with an accumulation of lactate. In well-trained endurance athletes the PR range within which energy supply is completely aerobic has strongly increased. The larger PR range within which energy is only supplied aerobically means a great aerobic capacity. This great aerobic capacity enables the athlete to maintain an endurance exertion longer and at a higher pace. The athlete has more stamina. Only for exertions with a very high intensity the anaerobic system is called upon, with the nasty consequence of lactate accumulation.

The pulse rate-lactate curve

The pulse rate lactate curve is different for every individual. Especially a change in state of conditioning influences the course of the curve. The left-hand curve is one of an untrained person. His deflection point is at a PR of 130 beats per minute.
The right-hand curve shows that after a period of training, the PR at the deflection point has shifted to 180 beats per minute.

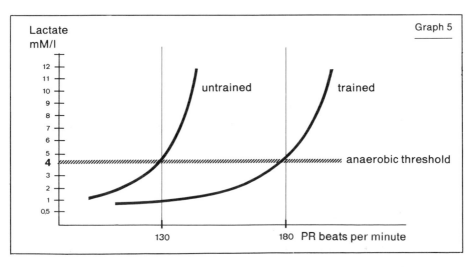

The untrained person can maintain an exertion for a long time at a PR of not more than 130. The trained athlete can perform a long time at a PR 180. This intensity of exertion has turned out to correspond with a blood lactate content of 4 millimoles per liter.

This point is also called the anaerobic threshold. An exertion beyond the level of the anaerobic threshold is accompanied by a strong increase of lactate content.

Hans Koeleman, 3000 m steeple chase runner, during the Seoul Olympics.
Duration of the exercise 8 min. 30. Anaerobic energy supply is considerable. The race is run with high to maximum PR values. Lactate values reached during the race are high.

THE CONCEPT VO₂ MAX.

VO_2 max. is oxygen uptake during maximum exertion. $\dot{V}O_2$ max. is expressed in liters/minute. A performance at the level of $\dot{V}O_2$ max. can only be maintained for a very short time, a few minutes at the most.

During a $\dot{V}O_2$ max. exertion energy supply is aerobic and anaerobic. As the anaerobic energy supply has only a limited capacity, the test person will see himself forced to run or cycle slower after a short time. Endurance loads must therefore be at a level under the level of $\dot{V}O_2$ max.

Under the influence of training $\dot{V}O_2$ max. is increased. But what is more important is the fact that training also influences energy supply, making it more aerobic for increasing workloads.

Anaerobic metabolism comes into action at a higher percentage of the $\dot{V}O_2$ max. This means that, under the influence of training, lactate is formed at a workload corresponding to a higher percentage of the $\dot{V}O_2$ max. So training increases $\dot{V}O_2$ max. itself, but it also considerably increases the percentage of the $\dot{V}O_2$ max. at which an exertion can be maintained a long time.

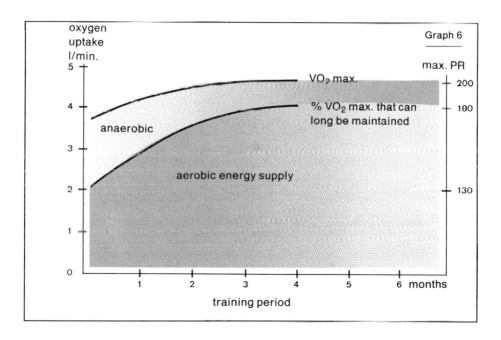

The right-hand vertical line shows the shift of the deflection point after a training period. When untrained, the PR at the deflection point is 130. After a training period of some months the deflection point shifts to 180 beats per minute.

PULSE AT REST OR MORNING PULSE

The pulse at rest or morning pulse may give the athlete or his coach information about the state of conditioning. More important, however, is the information thus obtained about recovery after a race or workout. Overtraining may then be tracked at a very early phase.

Also ongoing or insufficiently healed infections, such as all virus infections (colds/flus), can be established by registrating the pulse at rest. Every athlete who takes his sport seriously should draw up a pulse curve (see curve 1). Improvements in the state of conditioning go together with a gradual drop of the pulse rate at rest.

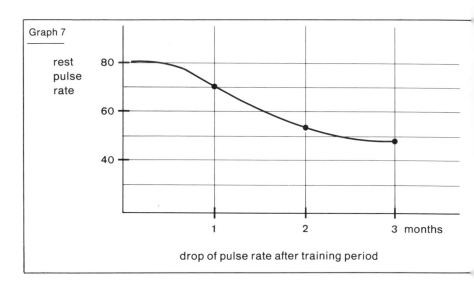

Graph 7

rest pulse rate

drop of pulse rate after training period

Counting pulse rate

The best place to count PR is the wrist, the left side of the chest, on the place where the heart is or beside the throat. Count the heart beats during 15 seconds and multiply that number by 4 to obtain the number of beats per minute. So when 12 heartbeats are counted in 15 seconds, the PR per minute is 4 x 12 = 48 beats.

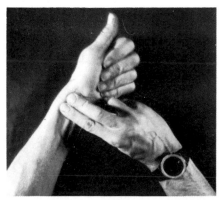

Counting pulse at rest

The pulse at rest is counted in the morning before getting up out of bed. Thus the circumstances under which the counting takes place are always equal. The data obtained are presented in a curve.

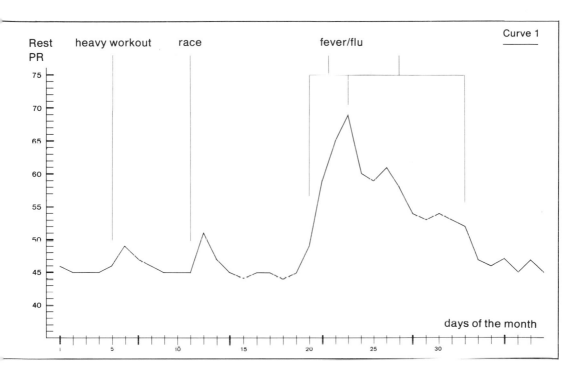

Counting the pulse immediately after exercise

The exertion pulse rate can best be counted with the 10 beats time. Immediately after the exertion one clocks the time of 10 successive beats. From the table the PR per minute can then be read. Press the stopwatch at a beat (= 0) and count 0, 1, 2 etc. Press again at 10.

TIME sec.	PR beats/min.	TIME sec.	PR beats/min.	TIME sec.	PR beats/min.
3.1	194	4.1	146	5.1	118
3.2	188	4.2	143	5.2	115
3.3	182	4.3	140	5.3	113
3.4	177	4.4	136	5.4	111
3.5	171	4.5	133	5.5	109
3.6	167	4.6	130	5.6	107
3.7	162	4.7	128	5.7	105
3.8	158	4.8	125	5.8	103
3.9	154	4.9	122	5.9	102
4.0	150	5.0	120	6.0	100

The PR value gives the number of beats you have per minute at that moment.

27

THE INFLUENCE OF AGE ON MAXIMUM PULSE RATE

When you grow older a gradual decrease of your maximum PR takes place. This decrease does not depend on the state of conditioning. A person of 20 may reach a maximum PR of 220 beats per minute. At an age of 40 the maximum attainable PR is often not higher than 180 beats per minute. There are rather large differences in maximum PR between individuals of the same age. Thus one 40-year-old person may have a maximum PR of about 165 beats per minute, and another man of the same age may have 185 beats per minute.

As age increases, a linear decrease of maximum pulse rate takes place.

The formula is: PR max. = 220 − age (in years).

So a forty-year-old person will have a PR max. of 220 − 40 = 180.

In spite of rather many exceptions to this rule it is a fairly reliable rule-of-thumb.

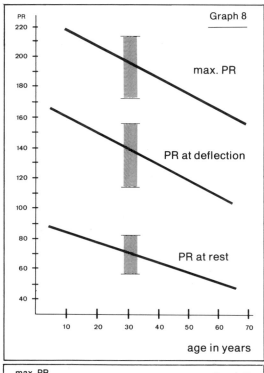

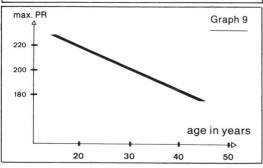

Veteran Eric Marsh (Great Britain) began endurance sports at the age of 59; he became a creditable marathon runner.

Not only does maximum pulse rate show a linear decrease with increasing age. Also, the pulse rate at rest, the pulse rate at the deflection point and the anaerobic threshold decrease with age. The vertical bars indicate how large differences between individuals of the same age may be.

THE INFLUENCE OF AGE ON THE DEFLECTION PR

Whatever goes for the maximum PR also goes for PR at the deflection point. When you grow older, the PR at the deflection point gradually decreases. Here again there are large individual differences.

Curve 2
Registration of an endurance run at racing pace of over 3 hours by a 42-year-old triathlete.

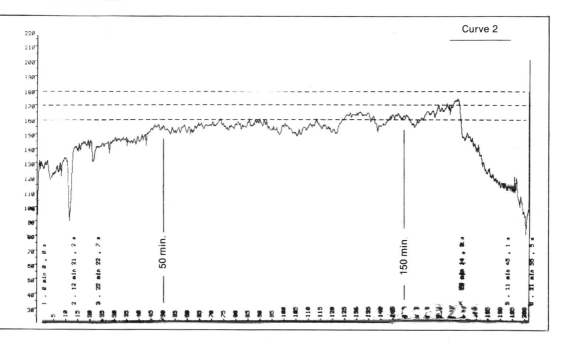

During most of the exertion, the PR fluctuates around 160. In his laboratory test this triathlete reaches a maximum PR of 187 beats per minute on a bicycle ergometer.
His deflection PR was calculated at 160 beats per minute. For a 42 year old man this triathlete has a high maximum PR.
The first piece of the endurance run, up to about 50 minutes could have been done faster, since this athlete's deflection PR was established at a PR of 160. This value was not reached by far in the first 50 minutes. The intensity of the run between the 50-150th minute is optimal. The PR is always very close to the deflection point. At the final part of this endurance run the athlete turned out to have some reserves left. He is then able to run for a considerable time with a PR higher than the deflection point. The calculated deflection point of this athlete was established in a sportspecific test which will be discussed later.

Curve 3
Registration of one hour, at racing pace, in a marathon runner of 42 years old.
His maximum PR, which is reached in a sportspecific test is 167 beats per minute. The PR at the deflection point was calculated at 142. As opposed to the athlete of curve 1 this marathoner has a rather low max. PR for his age.

29

The deflection point calculated for the marathoner is considerably lower for that matter. The marathon runner has done an excellent endurance workout with a PR which is always close to 140 per minute. He runs just below his PR at his deflection point.

The data of these two well-trained athletes show how large the variations between different individuals of the same age may be. The triathlete will have to train his endurance capacity at a PR very different from that of the marathon runner.

Curve 3

THE INFLUENCE OF STATE OF CONDITIONING, ILLNESS AND OVERTRAINING ON THE PULSE RATE

When somebody is overtrained his maximum attainable pulse rate will show a decrease. The maximum PR will also decrease somewhat in exceedingly well-trained endurance athletes.

The pulse rate at rest will distinctly decrease in well-trained endurance athletes. But when overtrained or ill, this pulse rate at rest will rise again. The PR at the deflection point settles at a higher level when the athlete is better trained. But also this level is distinctly decreased when the athlete is overtrained or ill. *See also graph 24 in the chapter: Conconi's test.*

INCREASE OF EXERTION PR AFTER RECENT BRONCHITIS, IN A MARATHON RUNNER

Test data: Lactate 2 = PR 155   Maximum PR = 180
Lactate 3 = PR 160
Lactate 4 = PR 163

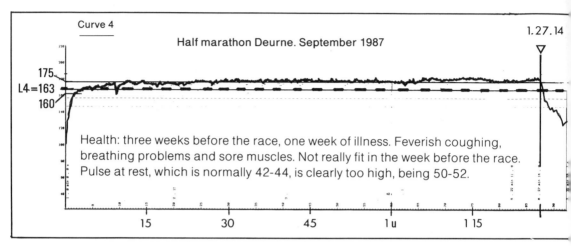

Curve 4

Half marathon Deurne. September 1987

1.27.14

L4=163

Health: three weeks before the race, one week of illness. Feverish coughing, breathing problems and sore muscles. Not really fit in the week before the race. Pulse at rest, which is normally 42-44, is clearly too high, being 50-52.

Race: did not run well. Very high PR at relatively low pace, PR being 175. Time 1.27.14. Poor recovery after race.

Conclusion:
Performance capacity clearly goes down when insufficiently recovered after an infectious disease. When doing exercise, PR goes up higher than normal values at relatively low speed.

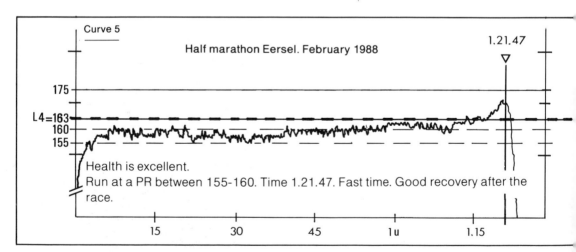

Curve 5

Half marathon Eersel. February 1988

1.21.47

L4=163

Health is excellent.
Run at a PR between 155-160. Time 1.21.47. Fast time. Good recovery after the race.

Conclusion:
Conditioning has strongly increased. It only makes sense to train or race when recovery after infectious disease is complete.
An exertion as shown in curve 1 is no good at all. It would have been better not to run the race and take a good rest instead or do a light training workout at the most.

THE INFLUENCE OF INSUFFICIENT RECOVERY, AFTER HEAVY EXERCISE, ON THE PR

An athlete has a maximum PR, a PR at a certain deflection point and a PR at rest. When fully recovered, these various PR levels are fairly constant. The day after a heavy workout the PR at rest may have risen. This signal, the rise of PR at rest, indicates that the body has not yet sufficiently recovered from the exertion. It may be wiser then not to do any heavy training on that day, thus giving the body a chance to recover. The benefits of heavy training in a period of insufficient recovery are always negative. Improvement of the physical condition does not take place and the level of performance even drops. Any exhausting training at a moment when incomplete recovery is noticed will in the long run lead to overloading and overtraining. When the morning pulse is 10 beats higher than normal, this is an indication that recovery is incomplete. Not only does the morning pulse rise, the deflection PR and maximum PR vary as well. These two then settle at a lower level. In such a state the athlete is not capable of performing maximally and subjectively he feels he is not going well.

During the races I and III the athlete had recovered completely. Subjectively he felt excellent during the races. The maximum PR was high in the two tests. During race II he had not recovered well enough. Subjectively the athlete was not satisfied: 'sore legs'. The maximum PR was clearly not reached

In illustration some registrations:

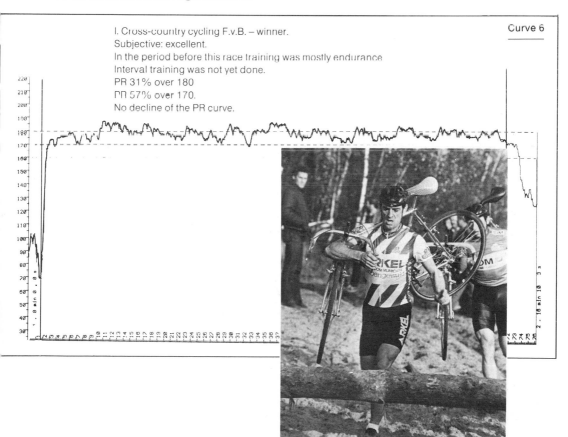

I. Cross-country cycling F.v.B. – winner.
Subjective: excellent.
In the period before this race training was mostly endurance
Interval training was not yet done.
PR 31% over 180
PR 57% over 170.
No decline of the PR curve.

Curve 6

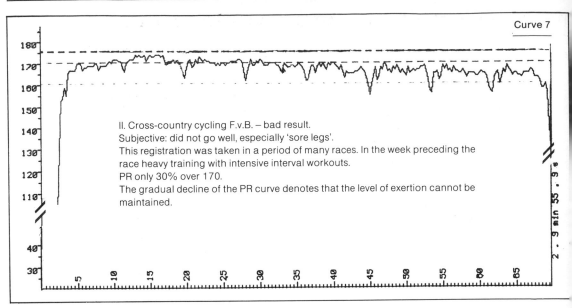

Curve 7

II. Cross-country cycling F.v.B. – bad result.
Subjective: did not go well, especially 'sore legs'.
This registration was taken in a period of many races. In the week preceding the race heavy training with intensive interval workouts.
PR only 30% over 170.
The gradual decline of the PR curve denotes that the level of exertion cannot be maintained.

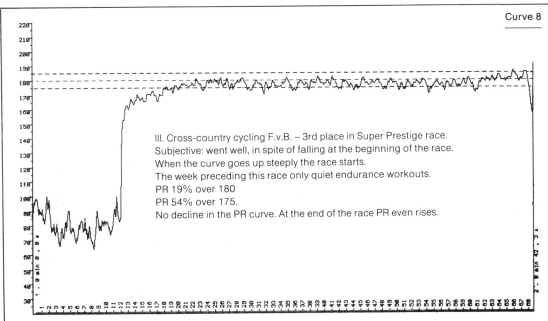

Curve 8

III. Cross-country cycling F.v.B. – 3rd place in Super Prestige race.
Subjective: went well, in spite of falling at the beginning of the race.
When the curve goes up steeply the race starts.
The week preceding this race only quiet endurance workouts.
PR 19% over 180
PR 54% over 175.
No decline in the PR curve. At the end of the race PR even rises.

Also registrations during the Tour de France and during the Netherlands championship team time trial at Dronten show very distinctly the decline of maximum PR and the deflection PR. During the Tour de France all cyclists are constantly in a state of overtraining or at least incomplete recovery, which can be seen in the PR curves (see curves 59, 62, 63).

Whenever morning pulse is 10 beats or more higher, or whenever the PR of a normal endurance workout cannot be reached or only be reached with abnormal effort, it is better not to force the body. The best solution is a recovery workout in that case.

THE INFLUENCE OF EXTERNAL FACTORS ON THE PULSE RATE

Air humidity and temperature of surroundings

All performances are also influenced by temperature of the surroundings and air humidity. For all workloads of whatever kind there are optimal conditions in the physiological sense as to external temperature and air humidity. Every physical performance depends on very complicated chemical reactions in muscles and nerves. These chemical reactions are very sensitive to fluctuations in temperature. Any change in internal body temperature will have its consequences.

In spite of the heat regulation center, the internal body temperature may be changed by means of muscular activity and high or low external temperatures. When body temperature is higher the processes in the body will be faster; when it is lower these processes will be slower. Pulse rate is one of the factors of that regulation and it is lowest at an external temperature of about 20 °C (68 °F). When at rest the body produces about 4.2 kJ (1 cal) per kg body weight per hour. During physical exercise heat production of the body may rise to 42-84 kJ (10-20 cal) per kg body weight per hour. Heat regulation is therefore heavily taxed. Pulse rate then rises, resulting in a better blood flow in the capillaries of the skin and a stronger production of perspiration.

An equal exertion at a body temperature of 37.0 °C (98.6 °F) or 38.0 °C (100.4 °F) shows a pulse rate increase of 10 to 15 beats.

Graph 10
shows the considerable effects of external temperatures on the pulse rate of a healthy test person at rest.

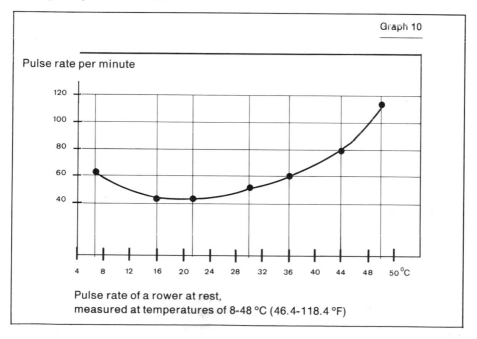

Pulse rate of a rower at rest,
measured at temperatures of 8-48 °C (46.4-118.4 °F)

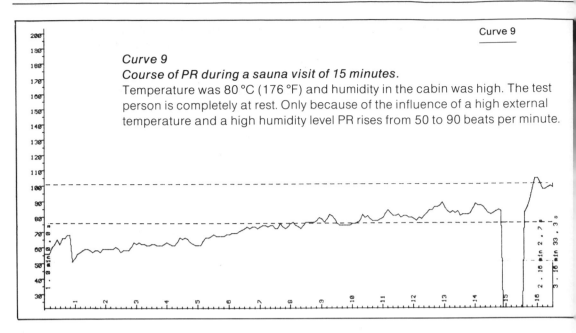

Curve 9
Course of PR during a sauna visit of 15 minutes.
Temperature was 80 °C (176 °F) and humidity in the cabin was high. The test person is completely at rest. Only because of the influence of a high external temperature and a high humidity level PR rises from 50 to 90 beats per minute.

Curve 10
Influence of external temperature on the PR
The curve is the registration of a 43-year-old marathoner with a deflection point at PR 175. The first part of the half marathon – till 40 minutes – is excellent. This part is run with a PR just under the deflection point. In the 35th minute a torrential rainshower begins; it had been dry before.
Because of this shower – external temperature had been 14 °C (57.2 °F) before – the runner cools down enormously and the PR cannot be maintained at the same level.

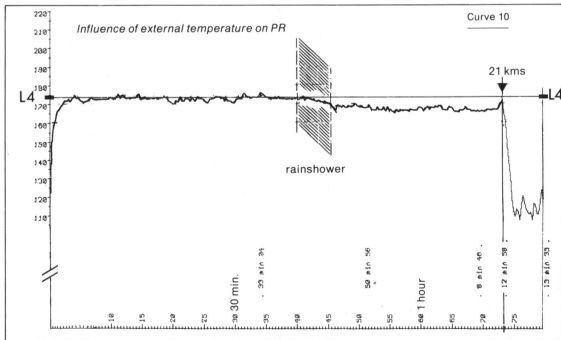

In high external temperatures and air humidity the body is more heavily taxed during physical exercise. With an equal level of exertion these factors cause a rise in pulse rate. As external temperature and air humidity rise the performance reserve for endurance loads diminishes.

The large amount of heat emitted by muscular activity leads to a higher internal body temperature in spite of the heat regulation system. This internal temperature rises as the workload increases in intensity and length and external temperature and air humidity rise. In these circumstances body temperature is clearly a performance-limiting factor. In general temperatures up to 20 °C (68 °F) are favorable for endurance loads. Higher temperatures between 25 and 35 °C (77 and 95 °F) are favorable for performances which tax the power-burst system, like sprints and jumping or throwing.

Through regular training at high temperatures the body adapts itself more or less, causing a less rapid loss of capacity. The heat regulation center may also be trained by visiting a sauna once or twice a week. Well-adapted clothing which does not limit heat loss and an adequate water intake before and during training contribute to maintaining a high performance level. When external temperature increases strongly, overnight pulse rate at rest or during exercise will always be higher. This goes together with a decreased performance capacity. After some days of acclimatizing with training adapted to it, the old level will soon be reached again.

Fluid loss and pulse rate

During physical exercise much heat is produced. Perspiration is an important form of releasing heat. Excessive fluid loss may cause some nasty complications. During endurance workouts body temperature may rise to 40-41 °C (104-105.8 °F). Body weight may decrease many kilograms on account of water loss. When this loss surpasses 3% of the body weight, body temperature rises and a life-threatening overheating may occur. With a body temperature of 41 °C or more, a so-called heat stroke may arise.

Important factors which may cause a heat stroke are high external temperature, high air humidity, slight body ventilation and no water intake in the hours preceding the exertion. It is of great importance to compensate fluid loss as well as possible by drinking 100-200 ml portions at short intervals. The quantity of

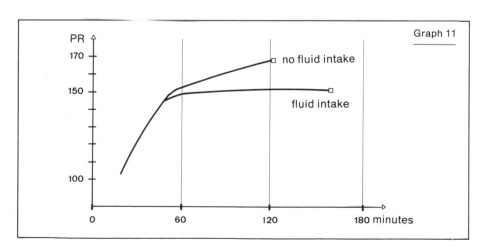

Graph 11

fluid lost may be estimated by regularly establishing body weight before and after training workouts.

During an endurance workout in the heat a water-loss of 3% of the body weight may already have arisen after 1 to 2 hours. For an athlete of 70 kg this means a fluid loss of 2.1 kg. This fluid loss causes a decrease of circulating blood volume, on account of which the input of blood in the heart is less. This diminished input is compensated by an increase in pulse rate. So fluid loss causes an increase in pulse rate.

The above curve is a representation of the course of pulse rate during an endurance workout at 70% of the maximum oxygen intake capacity. Outside temperature during the test was 20 °C (71 °F). When the runner was exhausted the test was ended. No fluid intake during the exertion caused a higher pulse rate. The moment of exhaustion was reached half an hour earlier. When the test person drank 250 ml every 15 minutes, pulse rate was maintained at a constant level. Stamina had considerably increased when the test person drank.

Influence of cooling during exertion on pulse rate

Fluid loss has an unfavorable effect on performance level. By drinking regularly fluid loss can be compensated.

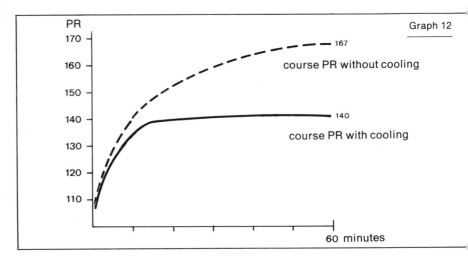

Also by repeated cooling during any exertion in hot surroundings, fluid loss may be restricted. Then the performance level decline will be less. From our own investigations the positive effect of cooling during exertion was clearly established. The same test person was tested with a 4-day interval on a bicycle ergometer, the first test without cooling, the second test with cooling. This cooling consisted of a ventilator and wet sponges with which the body was regularly wetted. The circumstances in the two tests were identical. Temperature 25 °C (77 °F). Relative humidity constant. The workloads of the two tests were equal. The total duration of cycling was 60 minutes. The course of the PR curve showed a clearly different picture. In the test without cooling, PR gradually rises from 135 to 167 beats per minute. During the test with cooling, pulse rate settles at a constant level of 140 beats per minute. Cooling may allow the exertion to be maintained longer.

38

Cooling during cycling and running

Cycling speed is greater than running speed. During cycling air cooling is therefore greater. This has a positive effect on the performance, the more so during hot weather.

Runners will sooner have problems than cyclists in hot weather. The slighter running speed goes together with less cooling. An increase of fluid loss will be the result, with all its nasty consequences. Cooling too fast with too cold water in too large quantities at a time works contrarily. There will be a cramp in the capillaries in the skin, this causing an obstruction to the release of surplus heat. The best way to prevent premature exhaustion during exertion in hot weather is drinking regularly and wetting the body regularly with a sponge.

The extreme consequences of dehydration during exercise in hot weather conditions. Loss of coordination, damage to the central nervous system. To be avoided through continuous cooling and fluid intake.

Influence of nutrition on pulse rate

Good nutrition during endurance sports may cause an improvement of the performance level. This improvement is expressed in a decrease of PR at equal workloads. Average PR with 'normal nutrients' $= 156 \pm 10$/min.
Average PR with 200 grams carbohydrates $= 145 \pm 9$/min.
As the exertion increases in duration the discrepancy between the two curves grows larger.

Graph 13
Course of the PR during a 2-hour workout on a bicycle ergometer.
With an intake of 200 gm glucose, PR during the complete test remains lower.

As the exertion continues, the discrepancy with the test group that does not consume extra glucose grows larger. The workload during this test is 70% of $\dot{V}O_2$ max. Performance improvement is 7%.

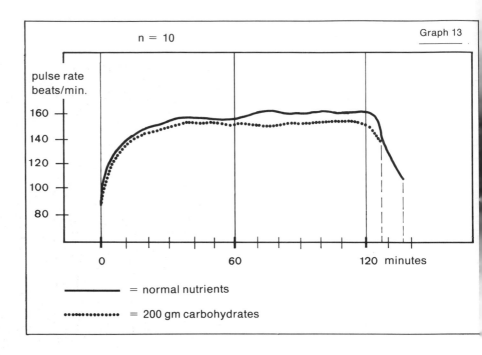

Graph 13

n = 10

pulse rate beats/min.

— = normal nutrients

•••••••••••• = 200 gm carbohydrates

Some other factors that influence PR

Altitude

The first hours after arrival at a certain altitude PR at rest decreases, then it increases. At 2000 m this increase is 10% and at 4500 m it is 50%, starting from individual rest PR at sea level.

After some days (depending on the altitude) PR goes down again to normal rest values, in many cases even below those values. Reaching the individual rest PR at an altitude is a sign of good acclimatization. Because PR can easily be counted, the degree of acclimatization can be established in a very simple way.

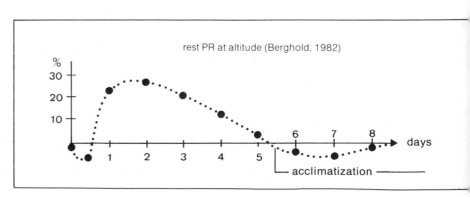

rest PR at altitude (Berghold, 1982)

acclimatization

For everybody who is at high altitudes for some time it is advisable to apply the following simple check-up method.

1. Take the morning pulse for some weeks prior to departure, thus establishing the individual value.
2. Take your pulse during your stay at the altitude in the same way, thus enabling yourself to establish the degree of acclimatization.

Dutch super-long-distance runner Bruno Joppen in the Swiss Alpine Marathon of 67 km, at 8000 feet altitude.

Medication

Various medicines influence PR. The best known are the beta-blockers. These beta-blockers are especially used against high blood pressure and angina pectoris. They decrease the PR at rest and also the maximum PR. (Angina pectoris: pain in the chest, mostly during physical exercise as a result of a stricture of the coronary artery.) When beta-blockers are used, endurance capacity is about 10% lower.

Beta-blockers are used as dopes in certain sports. In shooting sports beta-blockers are said to have a favorable effect.

The lower PR is less disturbing when aiming. The nervous trembling of the hands is also suppressed by these means.

41

ACCLIMATIZATION IN TROPICAL SURROUNDINGS

Basic data:
experienced marathon runner
recent deflection pulse: 176
recovery workouts: PR 140-145 (about 13 km/h)
endurance workouts: PR 150-160 (about 14.5 km/h)
intensive workouts: PR 160-170 (about 16 km/h)
tolerance workouts: PR 170-180 (about 17.5 km/h)
maximum pulse rate: 185.

Target:
marathon race in the tropics with 12 days of acclimatization.

Equatorial area in wet monsoon period; no direct sun, high air humidity of about 95%. Minimum temperature at nights 24 °C (75.2 °F), in daytime 30 to 37 °C (80 to 98.6 °F).
First registration after 3 days of adaptation to climate and time lag by means of short jogging runs.

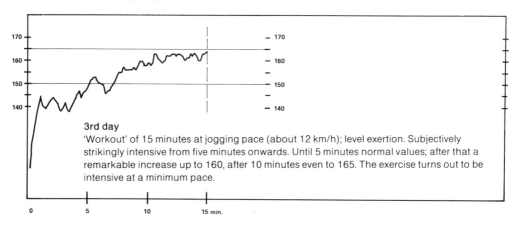

3rd day
'Workout' of 15 minutes at jogging pace (about 12 km/h); level exertion. Subjectively strikingly intensive from five minutes onwards. Until 5 minutes normal values; after that a remarkable increase up to 160, after 10 minutes even to 165. The exercise turns out to be intensive at a minimum pace.

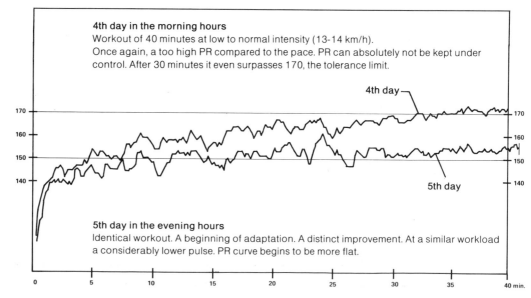

4th day in the morning hours
Workout of 40 minutes at low to normal intensity (13-14 km/h).
Once again, a too high PR compared to the pace. PR can absolutely not be kept under control. After 30 minutes it even surpasses 170, the tolerance limit.

5th day in the evening hours
Identical workout. A beginning of adaptation. A distinct improvement. At a similar workload a considerably lower pulse. PR curve begins to be more flat.

42

6th day

First longer workout is possible. 1 hour 20 minutes at 'normal' endurance intensity (13-14 km/h).

PR still too high for the intensity, range 155-165, but it is reasonably flat.

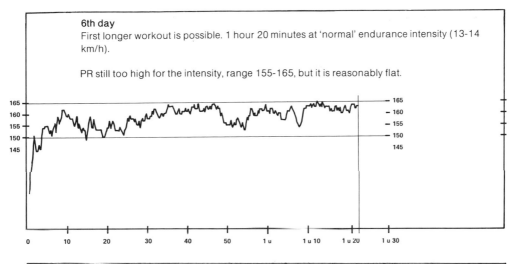

7th day

Longer endurance run, 1 hour 5 minutes. Still too high PR (13-14 km/h).

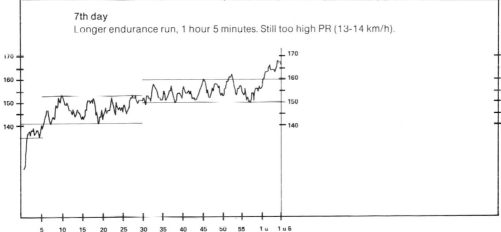

8th day

First extra-long endurance run, 25 km, 1 hour 25 minutes (about 13 km/h).
Tendency of steadily increasing PR is still there. (Note: despite decrease of the pace in the last 30 minutes to the minimum values of 12 to 13 km/h, PR keeps going up to tolerance level.)
The improvement in adaptation may be read in the duration of exercise that can be tolerated: two hours against one quarter of an hour in the first days.

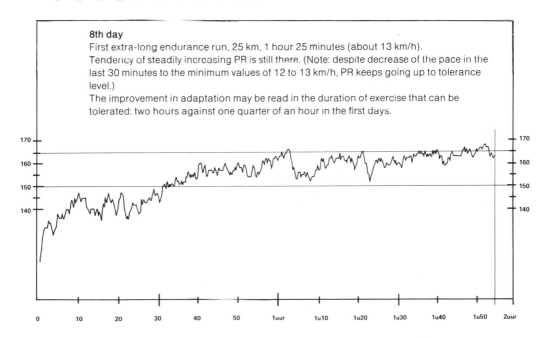

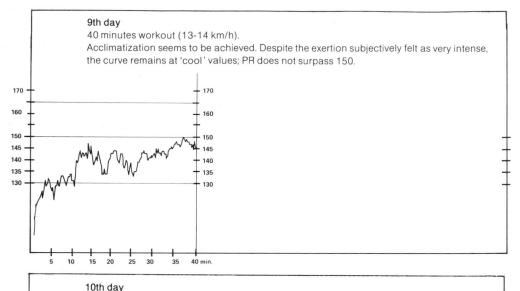

9th day
40 minutes workout (13-14 km/h).
Acclimatization seems to be achieved. Despite the exertion subjectively felt as very intense, the curve remains at 'cool' values; PR does not surpass 150.

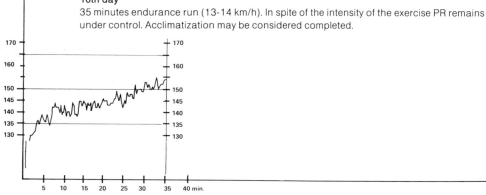

10th day
35 minutes endurance run (13-14 km/h). In spite of the intensity of the exercise PR remains under control. Acclimatization may be considered completed.

11th day
Day of rest before the marathon.
On the basis of the PR data of 11 days of acclimatization, the pace as well as the very high intensity it requires the PR during the race must not be higher than 160, which means that the expected speed cannot be more than 4 minutes per kilometer.

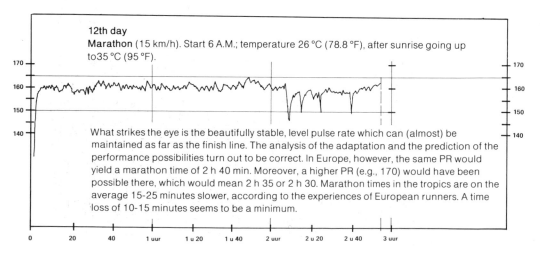

12th day
Marathon (15 km/h). Start 6 A.M.; temperature 26 °C (78.8 °F), after sunrise going up to 35 °C (95 °F).

What strikes the eye is the beautifully stable, level pulse rate which can (almost) be maintained as far as the finish line. The analysis of the adaptation and the prediction of the performance possibilities turn out to be correct. In Europe, however, the same PR would yield a marathon time of 2 h 40 min. Moreover, a higher PR (e.g., 170) would have been possible there, which would mean 2 h 35 or 2 h 30. Marathon times in the tropics are on the average 15-25 minutes slower, according to the experiences of European runners. A time loss of 10-15 minutes seems to be a minimum.

Schematic characteristics of acclimatization

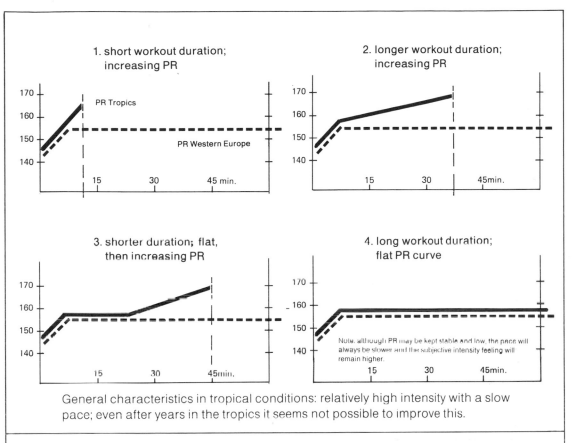

1. short workout duration; increasing PR

PR Tropics

PR Western Europe

2. longer workout duration; increasing PR

3. shorter duration; flat, then increasing PR

4. long workout duration; flat PR curve

Note. although PR may be kept stable and low, the pace will always be slower and the subjective intensity feeling will remain higher.

General characteristics in tropical conditions: relatively high intensity with a slow pace; even after years in the tropics it seems not possible to improve this.

Belgian runner Daniel Duprix, winner of the tropics marathon of Kuala Lumpur, Malaysia 1987

THE OXYGEN TRANSPORTATION CAPACITY OF THE BLOOD

An adult person has about 5 liters of blood. Blood can be separated into blood plasma and blood corpuscles. Blood plasma is a yellowish clear liquid containing the blood cells. Blood cells make up 40-45% of the total amount of blood. This percentage is called the hematocrit value of the blood.
Normal values for hematocrit (Hct):
Males: 42-54%   Females: 38-50%.
The largest part of the blood cells consists of red blood corpuscles, also called erythrocytes. The life-span of these erythrocytes is about 90 days. Each cubic millimeter of blood contains 4 to 6 million red corpuscles. The red color is caused by a ferrous protein hemoglobin, in short, Hb.

The hemoglobin may hold oxygen. One gram Hb can hold 1.34 milliliter of oxygen. As an average, 100 milliliters of blood (in males) contains 15 grams Hb (in females 12 gm Hb). So 100 ml blood can transport 1.34 x 15 = 20 ml of oxygen.
Normal values of Hb content:
Males: 8.7-10.9 mM/liter   Females: 7.5-9.7 mM/liter.
The red blood corpuscles can bind oxygen, and thus they form the oxygen transportation system. Whenever Hb content goes down from 10 to 9 mM/liter, the blood is capable of transporting 10% less oxygen. $\dot{V}O_2$ max. then also goes down by about 10% because it also depends on the oxygen transportation capacity. When oxygen transportation decreases, so does performance capacity.

Changes of the oxygen transportation capacity of the blood
Possible causes which might be of importance to athletes.
– Loss of blood.
– Lackof oxygen in the air.
– Blockade of Hb.
– Anemia.

Loss of blood
Oxygen transportation goes down after blood loss. Many athletes regularly give their blood as donors for the bloodbank. Per session 0.5 liter of blood is taken. After this blood donation it takes two to three weeks for Hb content to resettle at its normal value. During this period of recovery maximum endurance capacity is clearly less. So it is unwise to donate blood three to four weeks prior to an important endurance test.

Lack of oxygen in the air
Training at altitudes:
At high altitudes the air is rarefied and poor in oxygen. From 1800 m upwards, lowlanders are short of oxygen. The first period of their stay at high altitudes their performance capacity diminishes. The body needs time to acclimatize. During this acclimatization period the body gets a signal to produce more red corpuscles. After a stay of two to three weeks at high altitudes the results are noticeable. The number of erythrocytes has increased. Hb content has risen. The lowland level of performance can now also be reached at that particular altitude.
After returning to sea-level, the capacity of oxygen intake and transportation

has increased. The result: greater exertions can be done which can be maintained for a longer period of time.

Blockade of hemoglobin
Carbon monoxide (CO)
One of the disadvantages of smoking is that the Hb in the blood can be loaded with carbon monoxide (CO). This has a great impact on performance capacity of the body. Hb can hold CO about 200 times as easy as oxygen. So only a slight amount of CO is required to bring about a distinct decrease of oxygen-loading capacity of the blood. Inhaling the smoke of one cigarette has the effect that about 5% of the hemoglobin is loaded with carbon monoxide. The strong attachment of CO to Hb means that it takes hours before the CO has left the blood.

Heavy smokers often have more than 15% of their total quantity of Hb occupied by CO. On account of the decrease of O_2 content in the blood maximum O_2 intake also goes down, and with that, physical capacity. But not only smoking is a source of carbon monoxide. Exhaust gases from motorcars contain large amounts of CO. Therefore it is inadvisable to train in dense traffic or alongside a motorway. In race situations athletes and cyclists may be bothered by following cars and motorcycles. Just think of a breakaway group of cyclists going uphill in the Tour de France. They are swarmed by many motorcycles when they are performing maximally. The inhalation of carbon monoxide in such situations must be considerable.

Examples
On a motorway in Los Angeles an average of 55 p.p.m. (parts per million) CO is measured. If somebody stays one hour, while inactive, on or alongside the motorway, CO concentration in his blood goes up to 3%. After 8 hours this percentage has risen to 6%. During physical exercise breathing is quickened, which will cause the content of CO in the blood to go up even higher. From a CO content of 6% onwards serious complaints may be seen, such as diminishing of eyesight capacity, reaction speed and performance capacity. A CO content of

6% in the blood is reached after being exposed, inactive, for one hour to an air pollution of 100 p.p.m. CO. This concentration has often been found in Los Angeles in tunnels and near traffic lights. The accepted CO value in Los Angeles is 35 p.p.m. Above this limit the authorities give directives to decrease CO output.

Anemia

Endurance athletes often have anemia problems. This is caused by deficiency of iron. One of the characteristics of anemia is a decrease of Hb content, serum iron and ferritin content. Especially women are extrasensitive because of their monthly menstruation. The reason why endurance athletes so often have a deficiency of iron may be manifold:
– Nutrition may contain insufficient iron.
– The nutritional mix may play a role. Tea and coffee block iron absorption. Vitamin C enhances iron uptake. Vitamin C occurs especially in vegetables, fruit, potatoes and fruit juice.
   With meals it is advisable to drink fruit juices.
– During an exertion extra iron is lost through perspiration.
– While running, every stride is an impact which is felt in the footsole. This causes damage to blood cells, shortening their lifespan.
– After an endurance exercise loss of blood is often found via urine and evacuation.

In order to keep up the level of performance it should be avoided that endurance athletes develop iron deficiency.

Measures to be taken to avoid lack of iron.
– Nutrition should be varied. Together with the meals it is better to drink fruit juices.
   Ferrous products are parsley, broad beans, corn salad, red kidney beans, marrowfat peas and lentils, wholemeal bread, apple or molasses treacle, liver, pork and beef.
– Endurance athletes who train for many hours should regularly have their Hb, serum iron and ferritin content checked.
– If a lack of iron should arise it might be necessary to compensate it with ferrous medication.

It is an undisputed fact that a decrease of oxygen transportation has a negative influence on performance capacity. The opposite is also true. Literature shows that well-trained athletes may have an increase of 8 to 10% of their aerobic capacity after administering red blood corpuscles.

In order to reach an improvement of aerobic capacity of 8 to 10%, well-trained athletes should train intensively over a period of many years. Most of them will never reach such improvement. The differences between top athletes is only a fraction of the above improvement of aerobic capacity.

PULSE RATE AS A STANDARD FOR THE WORKLOAD

Two athletes running at the same pace, may reach a different pulse rate level. The conclusion that the athlete who reaches the highest pulse rate is more heavily taxed is not always correct.

Example: one runner has a maximum pulse rate of 210 beats per minute. His pulse rate during the run is 160 beats per minute.

His training companion has a maximum pulse rate of 170 and a pulse rate of 140 beats per minute during the run. The first runner is 50 and the second is 20 beats below their respective maximum pulse rates. In this example the second runner is taxed heavier.

Karvonen's formula is very suitable to judge the intensity of the workout.

$$\frac{\text{PR during exertion} \quad - \quad \text{rest PR}}{\text{Maximum PR} \quad\quad - \quad \text{rest PR}} \times 100\% = \text{.......} \%$$

Supposing that the two runners of the example have an equal rest PR of 50 beats per minute, their percentage of maximum workload is 69 and 75%, respectively. Karvonen's percentage is about 10% higher than the percentage of the maximum oxygen intake (VO_2 max.). So Karvonen's percentage of 75% corresponds with 65% of the VO_2 max.

TRAINING

The various energy-supplying systems and their meaning to different forms of training

Every sport knows its own specific forms of training. A marathon runner trains differently from a sprinter. The former will especially train a large aerobic endurance capacity, whereas the sprinter will be very interested in having an excellently trained anaerobic capacity.

Some sports performances, e.g., 400-m running require training of the lactate system. The 400-m runner must learn to fight against the strong acidification of his muscles and the feeling of fatigue that goes together with it. In so doing he trains his lactate tolerance. The aerobic endurance capacity can best be trained by endurance workouts, i.e., exertions lasting from at least 10 minutes to half an hour which are done at the same submaximal level. This level may very accurately be established and it is characterized by the fact that an accumulation of lactate does not yet arise.

An increase of the general anaerobic capacity can also be trained, of course. An increase of high-energy phosphates (i.e., creatine phosphate and ATP) is possible with submaximal interval work, the intensity being 80 to 90% of the maximum. These must be workloads with a duration of 10 to 20 seconds followed by a pause long enough to prevent high lactate accumulations in the body. The duration of the pause is one to three minutes, depending on the state of conditioning of the athlete (see curve 12 on page 77).

If the lactate system should be trained the duration of the submaximal working period should be lengthened to some 60 to 80 seconds. The short recovery pauses must not be that long that the lactate concentration in the blood strongly declines. This means recovery pauses of about 30 seconds to some minutes depending on the state of conditioning. Training of the lactate system as far as necessary, may best be done in the form of competition, it should be borne in mind, however, that two intensive races with one week's interval may be too much.

Such heavy workloads must always be followed by light workouts, the so-called recovery runs. In the above we mentioned lactate concentration in the blood a few times as a consideration. This concentration can be measured and it is expressed in the unit millimoles per liter (mM/l). Healthy persons at rest have values roughly between 1 and 2 mM/l. Performing at a high level may lead to an increase of lactate concentration, as has been said before. It ought to be known that this may have certain disadvantages.

Slight increases (6-8 mM/l) may influence coordination negatively. It may then be less easy scoring in football or soccer or performing in judo. It is even worse that regularly returning high lactate values influence the aerobic endurance capacity negatively.

Especially for this reason an athlete should be very careful with the number of intensive workloads that he takes upon himself within a certain period. The workload intensities, as used in the various training methods, can exactly be shown in a lactate workload curve (see graph 14).

The graph indicates the relation between lactate content in the blood and the intensity of the workload which is taken on for a certain period of time. For better understanding: this workload is here expressed in the form of speed, e.g., running pace.

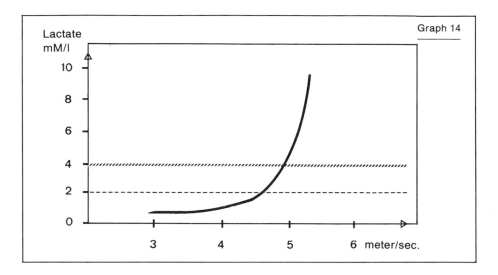

A lactate workload curve may be obtained by having the athlete run a certain route and then establishing the blood lactate value after every run. Every lap should be run at a constant pace and every new lap should be a little faster than the previous one. The length of the route should be such that it can be done in at least five minutes.

Low speeds go, in well-trained athletes, together with low acid values; the demand for energy can be met completely aerobically.
When the workload increases, the curve begins to go up; the working muscles do produce lactate, but the quantities are that small that they can be neutralized elsewhere in the body.

This is said to be the case with lactate concentrations between 2 and 4. This area is also called the aerobic-anaerobic passing zone. There is a certain pace which may be maintained for a long time without lactate accumulation in the body. If this pace is surpassed, a growing acidification will take place, depending on the degree and duration of surpassing; and there will be a time that the athlete will be forced to stop.
Lactate content measurable at this limit pace is also known as the anaerobic threshold. For practical reasons this is always assumed at lactate value 4 mM/l in the conviction that this value approaches the real threshold rather well. So performances over this limit pace lead to an increase of lactate in the body. The graph, which should be drawn up for every athlete individually, may be used for guiding his training.

It is known that stamina can best be trained by endurance training around the level of the anaerobic threshold, i.e., training paces corresponding with lactate values 2, 3, 4 and 5 mM/l, which can be read from the test results of the athlete. Very well-trained athletes train their endurance capacity at somewhat lower lactate values, mostly between 2 and 3 mM. Less well-trained persons improve their endurance capacity at somewhat higher values, around 3, 4 and 5 mM lactate.

Recovery runs are not intensive. Then lactate content is lower than 2 mM lactate.

51

Intensive interval workouts give high lactate values, going far higher than 4 mM lactate. This applies to more training methods. Under the influence of training the situation of the curve will change such that a shift to the right will occur.

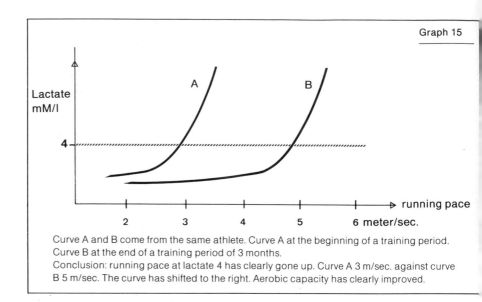

Graph 15

Curve A and B come from the same athlete. Curve A at the beginning of a training period. Curve B at the end of a training period of 3 months.
Conclusion: running pace at lactate 4 has clearly gone up. Curve A 3 m/sec. against curve B 5 m/sec. The curve has shifted to the right. Aerobic capacity has clearly improved.

Training intensity must therefore be readjusted every so often. New blood samples must then be taken. Not everyone can avail himself of this method unlimitedly.
But then there are other possibilities supplying the same or at least the most important information.

These possibilities, not requiring a blood sample, are:

– Conconi's test for runners and cyclists.
– The deflection point may be deduced after exact determination of maximum PR.
– Establishing the deflection point after an endurance run of one hour run at level pace.

All these methods are dealt with on the following pages.

LACTATE CURVES OF VARIOUS ATHLETES

The graph shows lactate curves of various athletes, all of them excellently trained. Every individual has his own curve and the mutual discrepancies often turn out very large. When the athlete with the curve furthest right trains together with the athlete of the left-hand curve and the two of them are told to perform at a pulse rate of 150 beats per minute, the left-hand athlete is going through a very intensive workout with high lactate values, whereas the right-hand athlete hardly exerts himself.

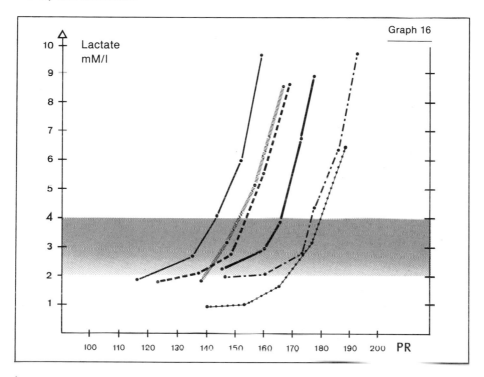

Training should be individually set. When training in groups, the training task has different effects on the various athletes.

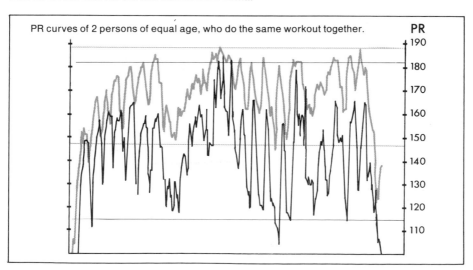

PR curves of 2 persons of equal age, who do the same workout together.

Individual differences

Fascinating individual differences in aerobic endurance have been measured in sports medicine institutes.

Graph 17 compares leading international women sprinters and long-distance runners. It shows the running speeds at which the threshold of 4 mM lactate/l is exceeded. It can be seen that sprinters have the lowest aerobic capacity and long-distance runners the highest.

The higher the running speed at which the lactate concentration exceeds the 4 mM/l threshold, the higher the aerobic capacity.

Graph 18 shows the differences in performance between a world champion professional racing cyclist, a world champion amateur racing cyclist, and a normal, untrained person.

The great difference between the top-class athlete and the normal person consists, firstly, in the enormous performance capacity of the athlete's heart, which in extreme cases can pump up to 40 l of blood/min., whereas that of the untrained person can only transport some 20 l/min. Secondly, the top-class athlete can employ the superior aerobic capacity of this skeletal musculature.

This superiority stems from the particularly large vascular surface of the capillaries in relation to the muscle mass and to the above-average size and number of mitochondria [5, 10].

The world's fastest woman, Florence Griffith

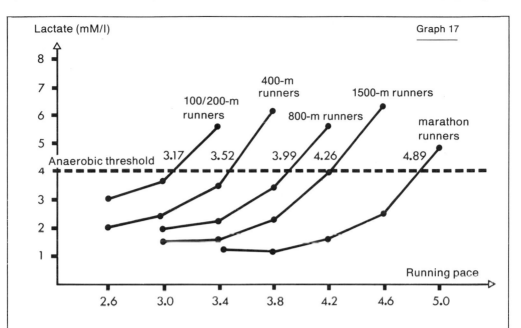

Graph 17. Running pace and anaerobic threshold in various top-class female athletes. The graph shows averages from different-size groups of top-class German runners.
(After W. Hollmann et al., Spektrum der Wissenschaft (1986), (8) 48-58.)

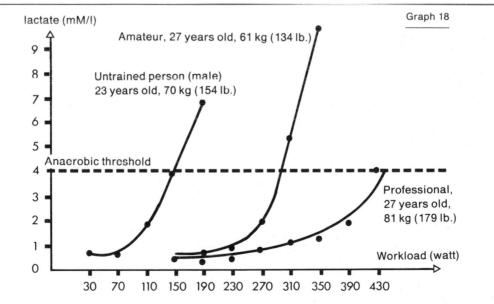

Graph 18. Differences in performance, assessed according to the height of the anaerobic threshold, with increasing workload in a bicycle ergometric exercise test.
(From W. Hollmann et al., Spektrum der Wissenschaft (1986), (8) 48-58.)

DISADVANTAGES OF LACTATE

High lactate values which may arise from heavy workloads may have disadvantageous effects. These high lactate values express the inability of the aerobic energy-supplying system. Energy supply from anaerobic sources springs into action.

High lactate concentrations cause an acidosis in and around muscle cells
This acid environment may seriously interfere with various mechanisms in the muscle cells. The aerobic enzymes system in the muscle cell may be seen as a factory where aerobic energy supply takes place. This enzymes system is sabotaged by acidosis, with as a result a decrease of aerobic endurance capacity. It may be days before this system has sufficiently recovered and aerobic capacity is at its old level again.

When the workload is repeatedly too intensive i.e., without sufficient time to recover, a considerable decrease in aerobic endurance capacity is inevitable. These too-intensive workloads then lead to a complex of complaints known as overtraining.

The acidosis causes damage to the muscle cell wall. This causes a leak from the muscle cell to the blood, e.g., an increased urea and CPK content as a sign of a leak in the muscle cell wall.

It may be 24 to 96 hours before these values have settled down again. Recovery of the muscle cell damage may last long. When choosing a form of workout, this should be a consideration. Workloads should be light in this situation: the so-called recovery or regeneration workout. Whenever training is too intensive, recovery will last longer.

High lactate values disturb coordination

Intensive workouts with high lactate values interfere with coordination capacity. Coordination capacity is of overall importance in sports requiring highly technical skills, as for instance soccer, tennis and judo. Training should not take place with lactate contents over 6-8 mM, because then coordination is disturbed to that extent that training these skills will have no positive effect whatsoever.

High lactate values increase injury risks

Through acidosis in the muscles, microruptures will arise in the muscular tissues. These minor damages will, if insufficiently healed, be the most important cause of bigger injuries.

The creatine phosphate system is disturbed by high lactate values

The re-formation of creatine phosphate is delayed in acid muscles. Therefore, this is an argument to avoid high lactate values during sprint training.

Fat oxidation stagnates at high lactate values

When glycogen reserves are depleted, energy supply is endangered at high lactate values because fat oxidation is slowed down.

INDIVIDUAL COACHING WITH THE HELP OF PULSE RATE

Starting from the lactate/PR curve it is possible to establish exactly at what PR an athlete should train.

The various training forms in relation to lactate concentration and PR

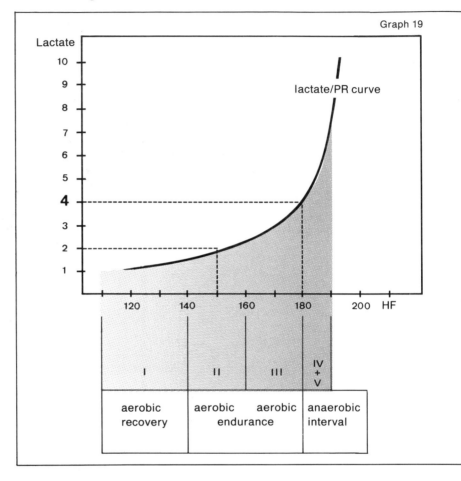

Graph 19

I **Recovery** or regeneration workout. Intensity of this training well under 2 mM lactate. In the example between PR 110-140.

II **Extensive endurance** workout. Intensity of this training around 2 mM lactate. In the example PR between 140-160.

III **Intensive endurance** workout. Intensity of the training between 3 and 4 mM lactate. In the example PR between 160-180.

IV **Extensive repetitions** (tempo duration) Intensity between 4 and 6 mM lactate. In the example over PR 180.

V **Intensive repetitions** (intensive repetitions). Intensity between 6 and 12 mM lactate. In the example PR over 180.

Optimal training of endurance capacity

With the help of pulse rate the intensity of endurance training can be set optimally. The benefits of training can be maximalized by it. By making a maximal use of training it may even be possible to improve performance level with less training.

Optimal training of the creatine phosphate system

Intensive forms of training such as training the creatine phosphate system and lactate system can reasonably well be set with the help of pulse rates. When training the creatine phosphate system, the following characteristics should be borne in mind. The duration of the load is short, viz. 5 to 10 or 20 seconds at the most. The intensity is high, being 80 to 90% of the maximum The resting pauses are long, as long as one minute or even longer when necessary. Lactate content should not surpass 6 mM during this workout. The aim of this training is an increase in the quantity of creatine phosphate.

Training of the lactate system

Training of the lactate system is also called resistance training or lactate tolerance training. Various forms of lactate tolerance training are possible.

Short intensive exertions
Duration from 20 to 180 seconds. Exertions are alternated by recovery pauses from 30 to 60 seconds. This recovery pause should not be too long as lactate content must not decrease too much. The strong acidosis arising during this form of training may cause damage to the aerobic capacity or endurance capacity.

Long intensive exertions
In this form of lactate tolerance training the duration of the exertion may be some 20, 30 or 60 minutes. The intensity of the exertion is just over the deflection point. There are no recovery pauses.
During this training lactate content surpasses 6. This form of training also has the risk of causing damage to endurance capacity. This form can best be trained during races.

All-round athle
Mirjam
Bestebreurtje

The various forms of training in relation to lactate concentration and running pace

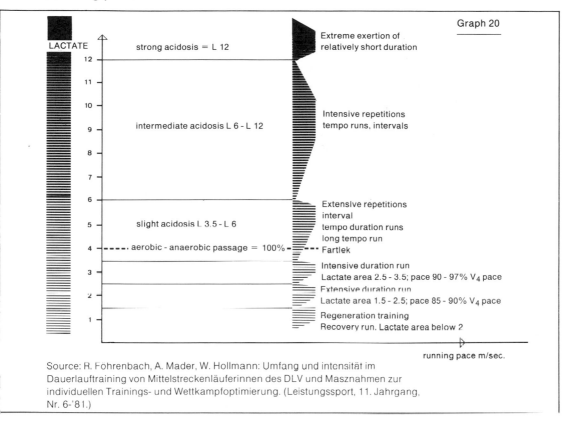

Graph 20

LACTATE

strong acidosis = L 12 — Extreme exertion of relatively short duration

intermediate acidosis L 6 - L 12 — Intensive repetitions tempo runs, intervals

slight acidosis L 3.5 - L 6

aerobic - anaerobic passage = 100% —

Extensive repetitions
interval
tempo duration runs
long tempo run
Fartlek

Intensive duration run
Lactate area 2.5 - 3.5; pace 90 - 97% V_4 pace
Extensive duration run
Lactate area 1.5 - 2.5; pace 85 - 90% V_4 pace
Regeneration training
Recovery run. Lactate area below 2

running pace m/sec.

Source: R. Fohrenbach, A. Mader, W. Hollmann: Umfang und intensität im Dauerlauftraining von Mittelstreckenläuferinnen des DLV und Masznahmen zur individuellen Trainings- und Wettkampfoptimierung. (Leistungssport, 11. Jahrgang, Nr. 6-'81.)

The notions extensive and intensive visualized graphically © Küsters/Janssen

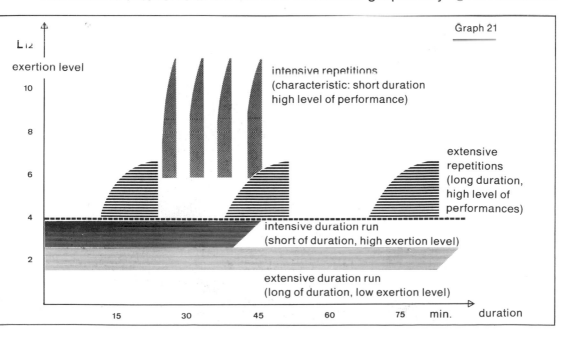

Graph 21

L 12

exertion level

intensive repetitions
(characteristic: short duration
high level of performance)

extensive
repetitions
(long duration,
high level of
performances)

intensive duration run
(short of duration, high exertion level)

extensive duration run
(long of duration, low exertion level)

min. duration

INTENSITY TABLE FOR RUNNERS

Explanation of the intensity table

Athletes who do not possess a sport tester may use the intensity table.
For this purpose the deflection point must be established with a lactate test or Conconi's test. A fairly reliable indication is also an endurance run at level pace of about one hour.

The formula is:
Distance covered in meters: time in seconds.

For example:
Distance covered during the hour run is 16,200 meters. The pace at the deflection point in meters per second:
16,200 : 3600 = 4.50 meters/second.

In the table this corresponds to 16.200 km/h. These 4.50 m/s or 16.2 km/h is the pace of the deflection point. This running pace is put at 100%. The marathon is run with an intensity of about 95%.* In the example the predicted marathon time is 166 minutes.

Because the values in the table are dependent on the everyday circumstances, they do no more than approach the value. The example runner would take 16.200 m ± 400. The various intensities are expressed in meters per second.

Often note your time per 200 m during your workouts. If you follow the above example (15.8 - 16.6 km/h), ER1 pace in the table is between 3.51 and 3.69 m/sec.

Calculated time per 200 meters:
200/3.51 = 56.9 seconds
200/3.69 = 54.2 seconds.

The ER1 pace is therefore between these values. The same formula may be applied to the other intensity levels.

---

* The exact percentage is 94.3. This result was obtained after our own research on some one hundred long-distance runners; it is in accordance with foreign research.

	Explanation:	
R	= recovery	time 90 - 120 min
ER1	= endurance pace 1 at lactate value 1 (mM/l)	time 50 - 90 min
ER2	= endurance pace 2 at lactate value 2	time 30 - 50 min
ER3	= endurance pace 3 at lactate value 3	time 20 - 30 min
100%	= lactate value 4 and anaerobic threshold	repetitions
100% and more	= tolerance training	intervals
95%	= marathon pace = lactate value 2.5+	

INTENSITY TABLE FOR RUNNERS IN METERS PER SECOND

Tolerance					Deflection point km/h		Endurance ER3		ER2	Recovery ER1	R	Mar. time
125%	120%	115%	110%	103%	100%	100%	97%	95%	91%	80%	75%	in min.
3.82	3.67	3.51	3.36	3.15	11.000	3.06	2.96	2.90	2.78	2.44	2.29	244
3.89	3.73	3.58	3.42	3.20	11.200	3.11	3.02	2.96	2.83	2.49	2.33	240
3.96	3.80	3.64	3.48	3.26	11.400	3.17	3.07	3.01	2.88	2.53	2.38	236
4.03	3.87	3.71	3.54	3.32	11.600	3.22	3.13	3.06	2.93	2.58	2.42	231
4.10	3.93	3.77	3.61	3.38	11.800	3.28	3.18	3.11	2.98	2.62	2.46	288
4.17	4.00	3.83	3.67	3.43	12.000	3.33	3.23	3.17	3.03	2.67	2.50	224
4.24	4.07	3.90	3.73	3.49	12.200	3.39	3.29	3.22	3.08	2.71	2.54	220
4.31	4.13	3.96	3.79	3.55	12.400	3.44	3.34	3.27	3.13	2.76	2.58	217
4.38	4.20	4.03	3.85	3.61	12.600	3.50	3.40	3.33	3.19	2.80	2.63	213
4.44	4.27	4.09	3.91	3.66	12.800	3.56	3.45	3.38	3.24	2.84	2.67	210
4.51	4.33	4.15	3.97	3.72	13.000	3.61	3.50	3.43	3.29	2.89	2.71	207
4.58	4.40	4.22	4.03	3.78	13.200	3.67	3.56	3.48	3.34	2.93	2.75	203
4.65	4.47	4.28	4.09	3.83	13.400	3.72	3.61	3.54	3.39	2.98	2.79	200
4.72	4.53	4.34	4.16	3.89	13.600	3.78	3.66	3.59	3.44	3.02	2.83	197
4.79	4.60	4.41	4.22	3.95	13.800	3.83	3.72	3.64	3.49	3.07	2.88	195
4.86	4.67	4.47	4.28	4.01	14.000	3.89	3.77	3.69	3.54	3.11	2.92	192
4.93	4.73	4.54	4.34	4.06	14.200	3.94	3.83	3.75	3.59	3.16	2.96	189
5.00	4.80	4.60	4.40	4.12	14.400	4.00	3.88	3.80	3.64	3.20	3.00	186
5.07	4.87	4.66	4.46	4.18	14.600	4.06	3.93	3.85	3.69	3.24	3.04	184
5.14	4.93	4.73	4.52	4.23	14.800	4.11	3.99	3.91	3.74	3.29	3.08	181
5.21	5.00	4.79	4.58	4.29	15.000	4.17	4.04	3.96	3.79	3.33	3.13	179
5.28	5.07	4.86	4.64	4.35	15.200	4.22	4.10	4.01	3.84	3.38	3.17	177
5.35	5.13	4.92	4.71	4.41	15.400	4.28	4.15	4.06	3.89	3.42	3.21	174
5.42	5.20	4.98	4.77	4.46	15.600	4.33	4.20	4.12	3.94	3.47	3.25	172
5.49	5.27	5.05	4.83	4.52	15.800	4.39	4.26	4.17	3.99	3.51	3.29	170
5.56	5.33	5.11	4.89	4.58	16.000	4.44	4.31	4.22	4.04	3.56	3.33	168
5.63	5.40	5.18	4.95	4.64	16.200	4.50	4.36	4.28	4.10	3.60	3.38	166
5.69	5.47	5.24	5.01	4.69	16.400	4.56	4.42	4.33	4.15	3.64	3.42	164
5.76	5.53	5.30	5.07	4.75	16.600	4.61	4.47	4.38	4.20	3.69	3.46	162
5.83	5.60	5.37	5.13	4.81	16.800	4.67	4.53	4.43	4.25	3.73	3.50	160
5.90	5.67	5.43	5.19	4.86	17.000	4.72	4.58	4.49	4.30	3.78	3.54	158
5.97	5.73	5.49	5.26	4.92	17.200	4.78	4.63	4.54	4.35	3.82	3.58	156
6.04	5.80	5.56	5.32	4.98	17.400	4.83	4.69	4.59	4.40	3.87	3.63	154
6.11	5.87	5.62	5.38	5.04	17.600	4.89	4.74	4.64	4.45	3.91	3.67	153
6.18	5.93	5.69	5.44	5.09	17.800	4.94	4.80	4.70	4.50	3.96	3.71	151
6.25	6.00	5.75	5.50	5.15	18.000	5.00	4.85	4.75	4.55	4.00	3.75	149
6.32	6.07	5.81	5.56	5.21	18.200	5.06	4.90	4.80	4.60	4.04	3.79	148
6.39	6.13	5.88	5.62	5.26	18.400	5.11	4.96	4.86	4.65	4.09	3.83	146
6.46	6.20	5.94	5.68	5.32	18.600	5.17	5.01	4.91	4.70	4.13	3.88	144
6.53	6.27	6.01	5.74	5.38	18.800	5.22	5.07	4.96	4.75	4.18	3.93	143
6.60	6.33	6.07	5.81	5.44	19.000	5.28	5.12	5.01	4.80	4.22	3.96	141
6.67	6.40	6.13	5.87	5.49	19.200	5.33	5.17	5.07	4.85	4.27	4.00	140
6.74	6.47	6.20	5.93	5.55	19.400	5.39	5.23	5.12	4.90	4.31	4.04	138
6.81	6.53	6.26	5.99	5.61	19.600	5.44	5.28	5.17	4.95	4.36	4.08	137
6.88	6.60	6.33	6.05	5.67	19.800	5.50	5.34	5.23	5.01	4.40	4.13	136
6.94	6.67	6.39	6.11	5.72	20.000	5.56	5.39	5.28	5.06	4.44	4.17	134
7.01	6.73	6.45	6.17	5.78	20.200	5.61	5.44	5.33	5.11	4.49	4.21	133
7.08	6.80	6.52	6.23	5.84	20.400	5.67	5.50	5.38	5.16	4.53	4.25	132
7.15	6.87	6.58	6.29	5.89	20.600	5.72	5.55	5.44	5.21	4.58	4.29	130
7.22	6.93	6.64	6.36	5.95	20.800	5.78	5.60	5.49	5.26	4.62	4.33	129
7.29	7.00	6.71	6.42	6.01	21.000	5.83	5.66	5.54	5.31	4.67	4.38	128

(research 'intensity tables' by Toon Wagemans)

INTENSITY TABLE FOR RUNNERS IN TIME PER KILOMETER

Tolerance							Endurance			Recovery		Mar.
							ER3		ER2	ER1	R	time
125%	120%	115%	110%	103%	100%	100%	97%	95%	91%	80%	75%	h/min.
4.22	4.33	4.45	4.58	5.18	11.000	5.27	5.37	5.44	6.00	6.49	7.16	244
4.17	4.28	4.40	4.52	5.12	11.200	5.21	5.31	5.38	5.53	6.42	7.09	240
4.13	4.23	4.35	4.47	5.07	11.400	5.16	5.26	5.32	5.47	6.35	7.01	236
4.08	4.19	4.30	4.42	5.01	11.600	5.10	5.20	5.27	5.41	6.28	6.54	231
4.04	4.14	4.25	4.37	4.56	11.800	5.05	5.15	5.21	5.35	6.21	6.47	288
4.00	4.10	4.21	4.33	4.51	12.000	5.00	5.09	5.16	5.30	6.15	6.40	224
3.56	4.06	4.17	4.28	4.46	12.200	4.55	5.04	5.11	5.24	6.09	6.33	220
3.52	4.02	4.12	4.24	4.42	12.400	4.50	4.59	5.06	5.19	6.03	6.27	217
3.49	3.58	4.08	4.20	4.37	12.600	4.46	4.55	5.01	5.14	5.57	6.21	213
3.45	3.54	4.05	4.16	4.33	12.800	4.41	4.50	4.56	5.09	5.52	6.15	210
3.42	3.51	4.01	4.12	4.29	13.000	4.37	4.45	4.51	5.04	5.46	6.09	207
3.38	3.47	3.57	4.08	4.25	13.200	4.33	4.41	4.47	5.00	5.41	6.04	203
3.35	3.44	3.54	4.04	4.21	13.400	4.29	4.37	4.43	4.55	5.36	5.58	200
3.32	3.41	3.50	4.01	4.17	13.600	4.25	4.33	4.39	4.51	5.31	5.53	197
3.29	3.37	3.47	3.57	4.13	13.800	4.21	4.29	4.35	4.47	5.26	5.48	195
3.26	3.34	3.44	3.54	4.10	14.000	4.17	4.25	4.31	4.43	5.21	5.43	192
3.23	3.31	3.40	3.50	4.06	14.200	4.14	4.21	4.27	4.39	5.17	5.38	189
3.20	3.28	3.37	3.47	4.03	14.400	4.10	4.18	4.23	4.35	5.13	5.33	186
3.17	3.25	3.34	3.44	3.59	14.600	4.07	4.14	4.20	4.31	5.08	5.29	184
3.15	3.23	3.32	3.41	3.56	14.800	4.03	4.11	4.16	4.27	5.04	5.24	181
3.12	3.20	3.29	3.38	3.53	15.000	4.00	4.07	4.13	4.24	5.00	5.20	179
3.09	3.17	3.26	3.35	3.50	15.200	3.57	4.04	4.09	4.20	4.56	5.16	177
3.07	3.15	3.23	3.33	3.47	15.400	3.54	4.01	4.06	4.17	4.52	5.12	174
3.05	3.12	3.21	3.30	3.44	15.600	3.51	3.58	4.03	4.14	4.48	5.08	172
3.02	3.10	3.18	3.27	3.41	15.800	3.48	3.55	4.00	4.10	4.45	5.04	170
3.00	3.08	3.16	3.25	3.38	16.000	3.45	3.52	3.57	4.07	4.41	5.00	168
2.58	3.05	3.13	3.22	3.36	16.200	3.42	3.49	3.54	4.04	4.38	4.56	166
2.56	3.03	3.11	3.20	3.33	16.400	3.40	3.46	3.51	4.01	4.34	4.53	164
2.53	3.01	3.09	3.17	3.31	16.600	3.37	3.44	3.48	3.58	4.31	4.49	162
2.51	2.59	3.06	3.15	3.28	16.800	3.34	3.41	3.46	3.55	4.28	4.46	160
2.49	2.56	3.04	3.13	3.26	17.000	3.32	3.38	3.43	3.53	4.25	4.42	158
2.47	2.54	3.02	3.10	3.23	17.200	3.29	3.36	3.40	3.50	4.22	4.39	156
2.46	2.52	3.00	3.08	3.21	17.400	3.27	3.33	3.38	3.47	4.19	4.36	154
2.44	2.50	2.58	3.06	3.19	17.600	3.25	3.31	3.35	3.45	4.16	4.33	153
2.42	2.49	2.56	3.04	3.16	17.800	3.22	3.29	3.33	3.42	4.13	4.30	151
2.40	2.47	2.54	3.02	3.14	18.000	3.20	3.26	3.31	3.40	4.10	4.27	149
2.38	2.45	2.52	3.00	3.12	18.200	3.18	3.24	3.28	3.37	4.07	4.24	148
2.37	2.43	2.50	2.58	3.10	18.400	3.16	3.22	3.26	3.35	4.05	4.21	146
2.35	2.41	2.48	2.56	3.08	18.600	3.14	3.20	3.24	3.33	4.02	4.18	144
2.33	2.40	2.47	2.54	3.06	18.800	3.11	3.17	3.22	3.30	3.59	4.15	143
2.32	2.38	2.45	2.52	3.04	19.000	3.09	3.15	3.19	3.28	3.57	4.13	141
2.30	2.36	2.43	2.50	3.02	19.200	3.08	3.13	3.17	3.26	3.54	4.10	140
2.28	2.35	2.41	2.49	3.00	19.400	3.06	3.11	3.15	3.24	3.52	4.07	138
2.27	2.33	2.40	2.47	2.58	19.600	3.04	3.09	3.13	3.22	3.50	4.05	137
2.25	2.32	2.38	2.45	2.57	19.800	3.02	3.07	3.11	3.20	3.47	4.02	136
2.24	2.30	2.37	2.44	2.55	20.000	3.00	3.06	3.09	3.18	3.45	4.00	134
2.23	2.29	2.35	2.42	2.53	20.200	2.58	3.04	3.08	3.16	3.43	3.58	133
2.21	2.27	2.33	2.40	2.51	20.400	2.56	3.02	3.06	3.14	3.41	3.55	132
2.20	2.26	2.32	2.39	2.50	20.600	2.55	3.00	3.04	3.12	3.38	3.53	130
2.18	2.24	2.31	2.37	2.48	20.800	2.53	2.58	3.02	3.10	3.36	3.51	129
2.17	2.23	2.29	2.36	2.46	21.000	2.51	2.57	3.00	3.08	3.34	3.49	128

RUNNING INTENSITY DEPENDENT ON DISTANCE
World records 1988

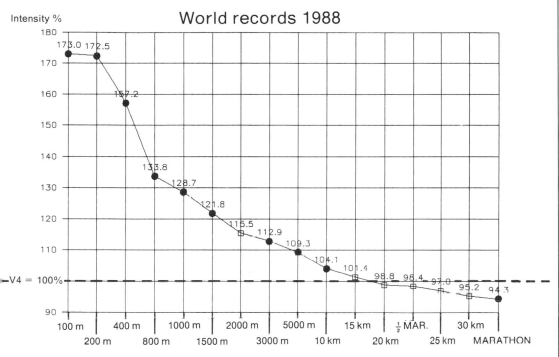

The world's fastest man, Ben Johnson

PULSE RATE/LACTATE TABLE FOR RUNNERS

There is a fixed relation between PR at the deflection point and the other training intensities.

Once the individual deflection pulse is known, the other training intensities can be found with the help of the pulse rate table for runners.

Pulse rate table for runners

PR/L 4	PR/L 3	PR/L 2.5	PR/L 2	PR/L 1	PR/L 4	PR/L 3	PR/L 2.5	PR/L 2	PR/L 1
140	137	134	132	122	171	167	164	162	149
141	138	135	133	122	172	168	165	163	149
142	139	136	134	123	173	169	166	164	150
143	140	137	135	124	174	170	167	164	151
144	141	138	136	125	175	171	168	165	152
145	142	139	137	126	176	172	169	166	153
146	142	140	138	127	177	173	170	167	154
147	143	141	139	128	178	174	171	168	155
148	144	142	140	129	179	175	172	169	156
149	145	143	141	129	180	176	173	170	156
150	146	144	142	130	181	177	174	171	157
151	147	145	143	131	182	178	175	172	158
152	148	146	144	132	183	179	176	173	159
153	149	147	145	133	184	180	177	174	160
154	150	148	146	134	185	181	178	175	161
155	151	149	147	135	186	182	179	176	162
156	152	150	147	136	187	183	180	177	163
157	153	151	148	136	188	183	180	178	163
158	154	152	149	137	189	184	181	179	164
159	155	153	150	138	190	185	182	180	165
160	156	154	151	139	191	186	183	181	166
161	157	155	152	140	192	187	184	181	167
162	158	156	153	141	193	188	185	182	168
163	159	156	154	142	194	189	186	183	169
164	160	157	155	142	195	190	187	184	170
165	161	158	156	143	196	191	188	185	170
166	162	159	157	144	197	192	189	186	171
167	163	160	158	145	198	193	190	187	172
168	164	161	159	146	199	194	191	188	173
169	165	162	160	147	200	195	192	189	174
170	166	163	161	148					

Various training forms and races related to the PR/L table for runners, visualized in graphs

Training workouts

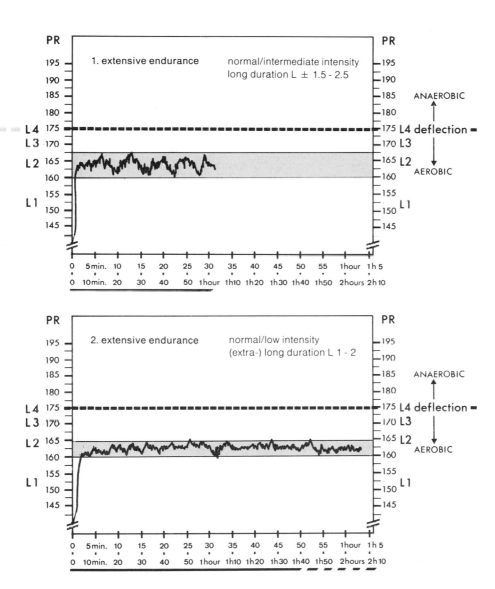

---

* The deflection point in the graphs is 175. The lactates derived are based on the pulse rate/lactate table for runners.

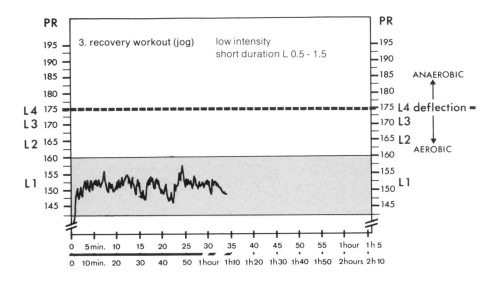

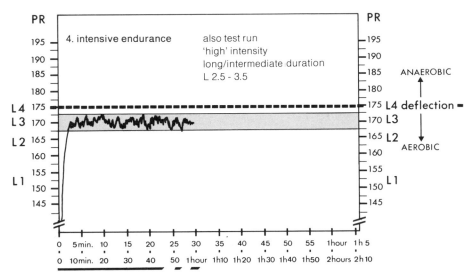

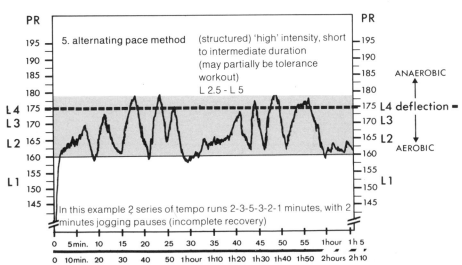

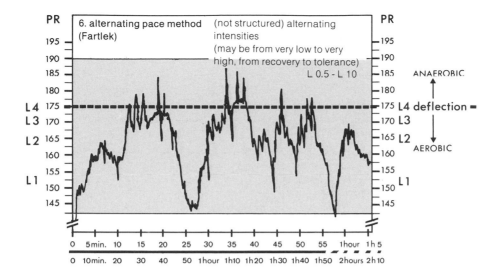

6. alternating pace method (Fartlek)

(not structured) alternating intensities
(may be from very low to very high, from recovery to tolerance)
L 0.5 - L 10

ANAEROBIC

L4 deflection =

AEROBIC

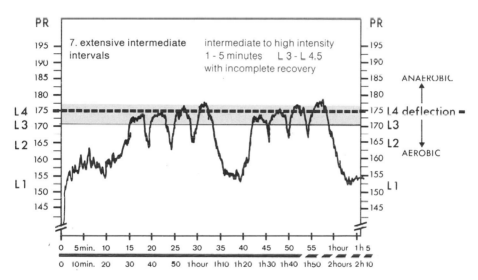

7. extensive intermediate intervals

intermediate to high intensity
1 - 5 minutes   L 3 - L 4.5
with incomplete recovery

ANAEROBIC

L4 deflection =

AEROBIC

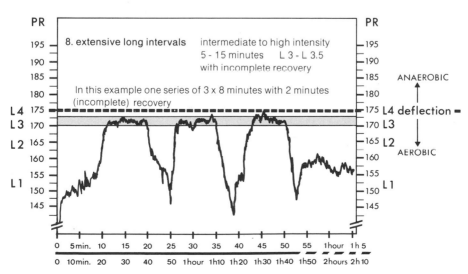

8. extensive long intervals

intermediate to high intensity
5 - 15 minutes   L 3 - L 3.5
with incomplete recovery

In this example one series of 3 x 8 minutes with 2 minutes (incomplete) recovery

ANAEROBIC

L4 deflection =

AEROBIC

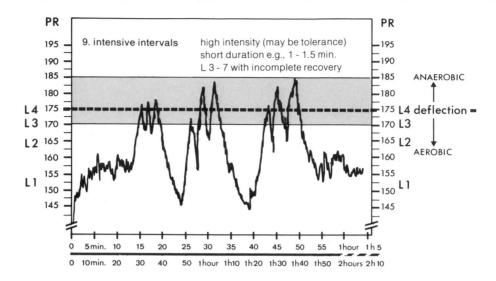

9. intensive intervals   high intensity (may be tolerance)
short duration e.g., 1 - 1.5 min.
L 3 - 7 with incomplete recovery

ANAEROBIC

L4 deflection =

AEROBIC

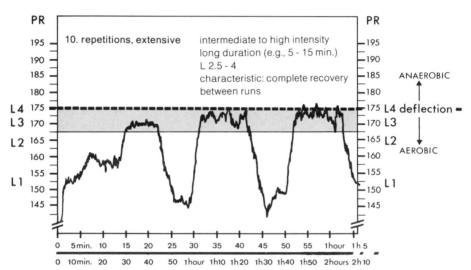

10. repetitions, extensive   intermediate to high intensity
long duration (e.g., 5 - 15 min.)
L 2.5 - 4
characteristic: complete recovery
between runs

ANAEROBIC

L4 deflection =

AEROBIC

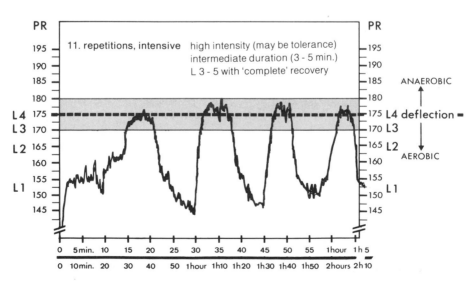

11. repetitions, intensive   high intensity (may be tolerance)
intermediate duration (3 - 5 min.)
L 3 - 5 with 'complete' recovery

ANAEROBIC

L4 deflection =

AEROBIC

70

Races

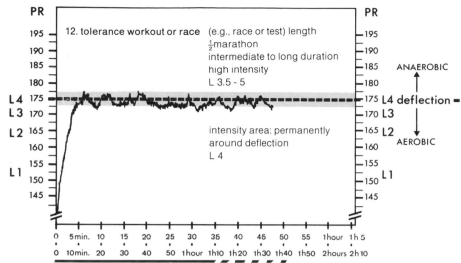

12. tolerance workout or race (e.g., race or test) length
½marathon
intermediate to long duration
high intensity
L 3.5 - 5

intensity area: permanently
around deflection
L 4

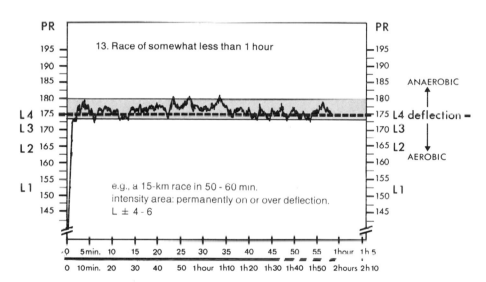

13. Race of somewhat less than 1 hour

e.g., a 15-km race in 50 - 60 min.
intensity area: permanently on or over deflection.
L ± 4 - 6

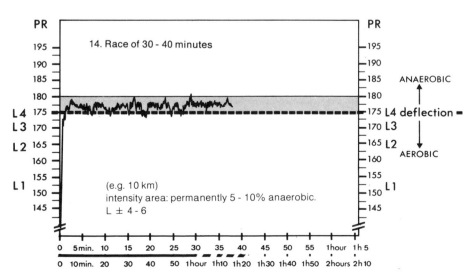

14. Race of 30 - 40 minutes

(e.g. 10 km)
intensity area: permanently 5 - 10% anaerobic.
L ± 4 - 6

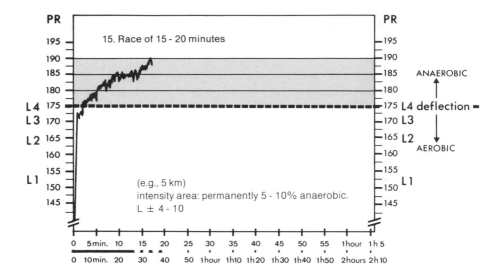

15. Race of 15 - 20 minutes

(e.g., 5 km)
intensity area: permanently 5 - 10% anaerobic.
L ± 4 - 10

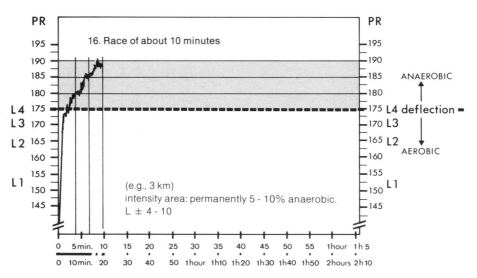

16. Race of about 10 minutes

(e.g., 3 km)
intensity area: permanently 5 - 10% anaerobic.
L ± 4 - 10

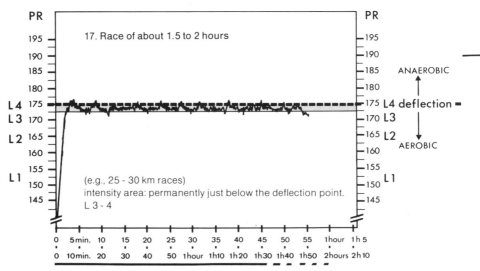

17. Race of about 1.5 to 2 hours

(e.g., 25 - 30 km races)
intensity area: permanently just below the deflection point.
L 3 - 4

72

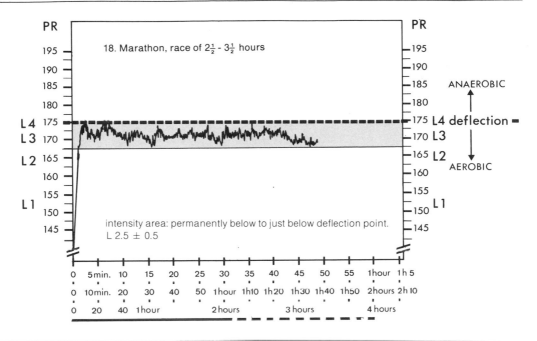

Olympic Marathon, Seoul. Top runners from left to right: Moneghetti (Australia) 5th, Saleh (Djibouti) 2nd, Ikangaa (Tanzania) 7th, winner Bordin (Italy) in 2 h. 10 min. 32, Kachapov (Soviet Union) 10th, Nakayama (Japan) 4th, Spedding (Great Britain) 6th, de Castella (Australia) 8th, Wakiihuri (Kenya) 2 nd.

MARATHON TRAINING FOR THE AVERAGE RUNNER

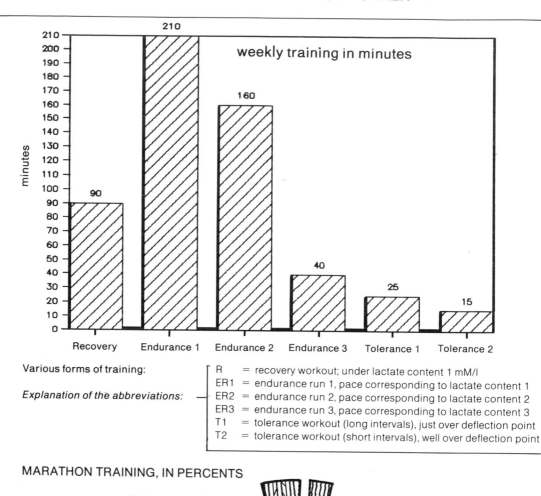

weekly training in minutes

Various forms of training:

Explanation of the abbreviations:

R	=	recovery workout; under lactate content 1 mM/l
ER1	=	endurance run 1, pace corresponding to lactate content 1
ER2	=	endurance run 2, pace corresponding to lactate content 2
ER3	=	endurance run 3, pace corresponding to lactate content 3
T1	=	tolerance workout (long intervals), just over deflection point
T2	=	tolerance workout (short intervals), well over deflection point

MARATHON TRAINING, IN PERCENTS

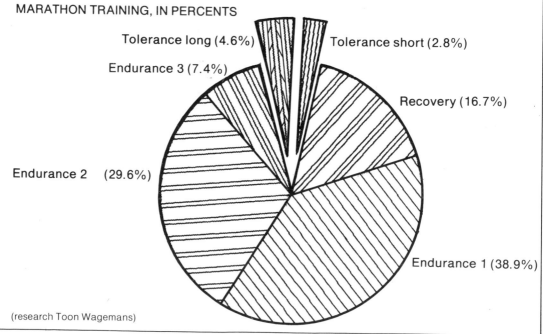

(research Toon Wagemans)

CONSTANT PULSE RATE REGISTRATIONS OF THE VARIOUS FORMS OF TRAINING

Training registrations

With the help of constant PR registration it is possible to establish objectively what kind of training workout an athlete has had.

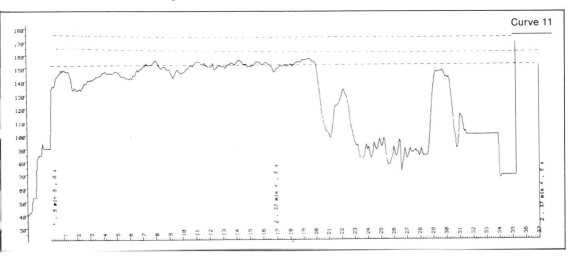

Curve 11
Recovery workout.
This curve is a reflection of a recovery run. Data of the athlete who was tested:
PR at lactate 4 is 175
PR at lactate 2 is 160.

During a recovery workout lactate values must not surpass 2 mM. Very well-trained athletes often recover well under 2 mM. This athlete is known to train too often too intensively. He has difficulty in controlling himself. Because of the too-intensive training workouts his performances in races are often disappointing. Therefore, he was told not to let his PR surpass 150 during this workout. Lactate content will then certainly not be more than 2.
If PR does surpass 150 during the workout, there will be a bleep signal. The athlete then knows he will have to slow down. As the workout was stored in the memory bank it was possible to analyze afterwards if the workout was carried out well.

Curve 12
Intensive endurance workout.
This curve is a registration of an intensive endurance workout on the road by a cyclist.
Data of this cyclist: during the bicycle test in the laboratory he turned out to have a deflection point L 4 = PR 164   L 3 = PR 157.
An intensive endurance workout for a well-trained cyclist takes place in the lactate area between 3 and 4 mM. During this workout PR constantly fluctuates around 160.

So this workout can be considered an intensive form of endurance workout. He

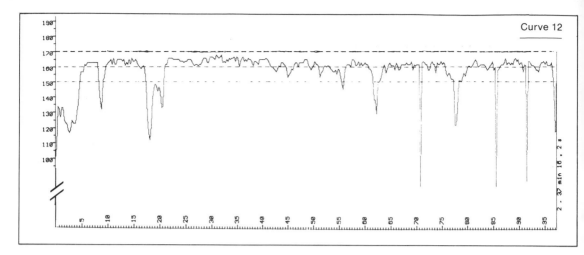

was told to maintain a maximally high pace for minimally one hour without allowing the pace to slow down. The downward peaks in the curve are traffic situations causing pace disturbances for a short time.

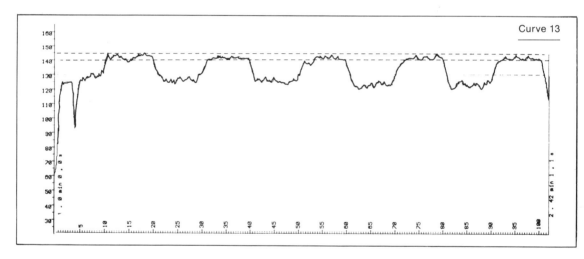

Curve 13
Example of an intensive endurance workout for a marathoner.
The task was running blocks of 10 minutes with a PR between 140-145. After this period recovery of about the same duration. This runner has a deflection point L 4 = PR 144   L 3 = PR 138.
The intensive part is always run with a PR between 140-145. Task was well done.

Curve 14
Intensive repetitions.
This curve is a registration of a workout by a cyclist on a bicycle ergometer. It is an example of intensive repetitions. His deflection point L 4 = PR 165.
Task: 20 x 10 seconds as intensive as possible alternated by 50 seconds of recovery.

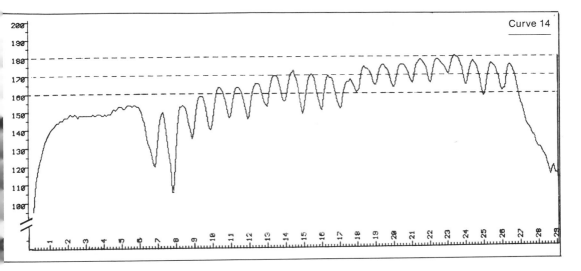

Lactate after 10 x = 7.4 mM. Lactate after 20 x = 9.8 mM. For a workout with intensive repetitions its intensity has been right: lactate content is between 6 and 12 mM. Notice that it takes long before maximum PR is reached. So in this workout the lactate tolerance capacity is taxed. This may be deduced from the high lactate concentrations that are reached.
If the aim of this workout had been training the creatine phosphate system it is too intensive. When training the creatine phosphate system such high lactate values must not be reached. These high values could have been avoided by taking longer recovery pauses, enabling the creatine phosphate system to refill. The first 6 minutes of the curve is warm-up.

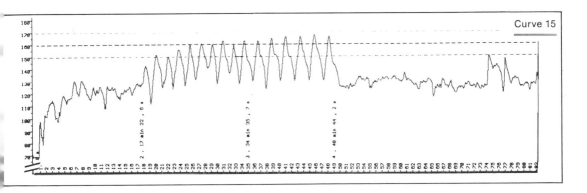

Curve 15
Another example of *intensive repetitions* for a cyclist in a so-called viaduct workout, having maximum exertions of 15 to 20 seconds followed by a short recovery pause.
Deflection point L 4 = 160.
Here again, maximum pulse rate is reached gradually.

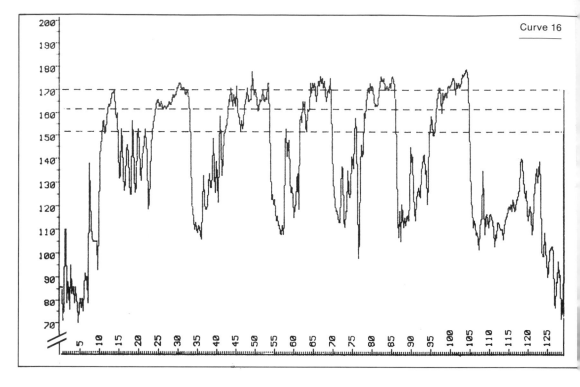

Curve 16

Curve 16

Example workout *extensive repetitions* during a cross-country cycling workout in a wood.

Deflection point L 4 = PR 165.

A number of blocks with intensity over PR 165.

Recovery pause long.

Lactate at end of workout = 10.2.

For an extensive training workout the intensity has been too high.

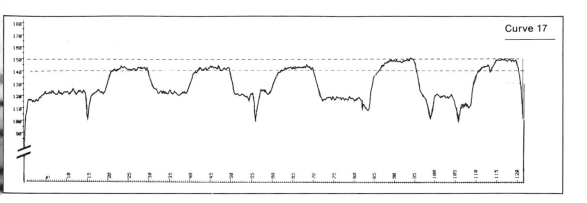

Curve 17

Curve 17
Example of a marathon runner.
The workout is a combination of intensive endurance followed by extensive repetitions.
Deflection point L 4 — PR 144.

Three blocks are run with a PR between 140-145 (intensive endurance) and then two blocks with PR around 150 (extensive lactate tolerance).
Long recovery pause between blocks.

CONCONI'S TEST

The following part is a rather complete representation of the article published by Conconi.

Conconi developed a method by which it was possible to establish the anaerobic threshold without measuring lactate, so also without taking blood samples: the so-called noninvasive establishing of the anaerobic threshold after Conconi's method. The anaerobic threshold (AT) may be described as follows: the AT is the highest intensity, e.g., running pace, which can be maintained for a long period of time. This exertion takes place at a certain percentage of the $\dot{V}O_2$ max. When this percentage is surpassed, an accumulation of lactic acid takes place. On account of this acidosis, the exertion cannot be maintained at this high level for long (see graph 6).

Conconi's methods were as follows: in a field test he established the correlation between running pace and pulse rate. For his test he used well-trained athletes. An ample warm-up of 15 to 30 minutes was followed by an uninterrupted endurance run. Depending on the protocol followed running, speed was slightly accelerated every 1000 or 400 or 200 meters; the increase being not more than half a kilometer per hour. After this acceleration the pace is kept at level speed. The pace at the start was 12 to 14 km/h, a pace which will be too high for many athletes. In every last part of 50 m PR is registered. By also registering the split-times, the running pace can easily be calculated. The pace, eventually attained is dependent on the state of conditioning of the athlete; it varies from 18 to 25 km/h. The relation between running pace (RP) and pulse rate (PR) is partly linear and partly non-linear. The pace at which the linear correlation between RP and PR is lost is called the deflection velocity (V_d) (see graph 22).
The time needed by PR to adapt itself to the new running pace is 10 to 20 seconds.

This only applies when the increase of the running pace is not more than half a kilometer per hour. The non-linear part of the RP-PR curve can better be established with the 200-m protocol, which increases running pace every 200

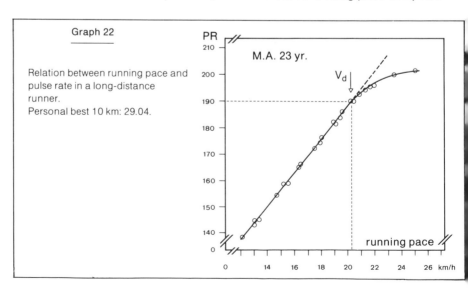

Graph 22

Relation between running pace and pulse rate in a long-distance runner.
Personal best 10 km: 29.04.

M.A. 23 yr.

meters. When this protocol is adopted, the number of registrations over the deflection pace is highest.

Graph 23 compares the three protocols.
The tests are done by the same runner. Personal best time for 5000 meters: 14 min. 12 sec. The total running distances of the three different protocols are 11 km, 6.4 km and 4 km, respectively. There was a resting period of three days between every test.

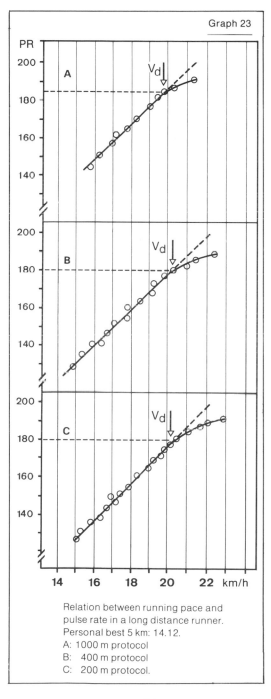

Relation between running pace and pulse rate in a long distance runner.
Personal best 5 km: 14.12.
A: 1000 m protocol
B: 400 m protocol
C: 200 m protocol.

Establishing lactate content of the blood at different running paces

First the PR-RP curve is drawn up. Starting from this curve, various paces are chosen, which should be run during the test. Three paces under the deflection speed (V_d) and three paces over V_d. Every running pace is gradually reached and maintained for 1200 m. By this gradual beginning lactate accumulation of the start (because of dysfunctioning of the aerobic system at the onset of the exercise) is avoided. At the end of every 1200 meters a blood sample is taken from a blood vessel for establishing lactate content.

Every period of 1200 meters is followed by a cooling-down period of 15 minutes. Graph 25 shows a comparison between the lactate curve found here and the PR-RP curve. The relation between the deflection pace V_d and the anaerobic threshold is clearly shown.

Results

The typical relation between RP and PR is seen in graph 22. RP and PR in this example are linear up to 20.1 km/h. At a higher pace (over V_d) there is a deflection in the curve. The same RP-PR curve is found when the athlete follows different protocols; see graph 23. The deflection pace found does not depend on the protocol adopted.

Graph 23
A V_d is established during a 10-km endurance run. Running pace is increased every 1000 m. Every kilometer is run at a level pace.
B The same principle but now the pace is increased every 400 m. Every 400-m lap is run at level pace.
C The same principle; the pace is now increased every 200 m. Every 200 m is run at level pace.
The V_d of the 1000 m turns out somewhat lower, viz. 0.4 km/h.

In well-trained athletes the PR at the deflection pace (V_d) is 5 to 20 (average 10.6) beats per minute lower than maximum PR. In untrained persons PR at the V_d is 20 to 27 beats per minute lower than maximum PR.

When the field test is repeated after some days with the same person and the circumstances are constant, the same test results are found. The test can therefore be reproduced a number of times. Conconi gives a correlation coefficient of as much as 0.99.

Graph 24
Change in the RP-PR curve after a training period in 2 runners (A and B).
The third test on S.A. (B) was done some days before the outbreak of infectious mononucleosis. When condition improves, when overtrained, or with infections there is a change in RP-PR curve.

Deflection pace (V_d) and anaerobic threshold (AT)

Graph 25 shows the results of a test on a 5000-m runner. V_d and AT correspond

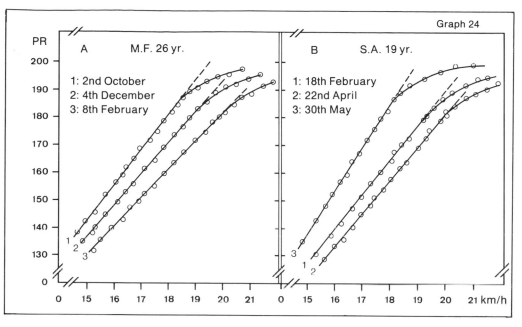

Graph 24

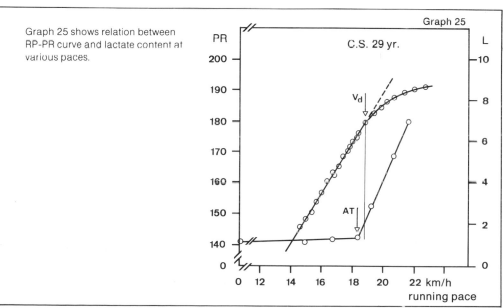

Graph 25 shows relation between RP-PR curve and lactate content at various paces.

Graph 25

well. There is a good correlation between these two values.

The V_d and the pace of various races are investigated in marathoners, one-hour runners and 5000-m runners. The field tests are done some days before the race. There is a constant relation between V_d and the pace during the various races. Also in other sports such as canoeing, rowing, cycling, roller-skating and cross-country skiing there is a distinct correlation between V_d and AT.

Discussion

The linear relation between RP and PR is lost at fast paces. There is a distinct relation between V_d and AT. An increase in pace over V_d and AT goes together with a fast increase of lactate concentration. This lactate accumulation is a signal of the lack of aerobic energy supply. Anaerobic energy supply assists as a kind of emergency system. By Conconi's method the AT of runners can be established without taking blood samples.

A maximum effort can be maintained only for a short time. In other words, $\dot{V}O_2$ max. can be kept for a short time, but then endurance efforts are done at a certain percentage of $\dot{V}O_2$ max. When this percentage is surpassed, there is an increase of lactic acid content, causing the athlete to stop performing at the same high level.

Not very well-trained athletes perform in endurance efforts at 50% of their $\dot{V}O_2$ max. Well-trained athletes are capable of performing for hours at 80% of their $\dot{V}O_2$ max.

The anaerobic threshold can be used for establishing the intensity at which the athlete trains his endurance capacity best.

There is a very significant correlation between V_d and running pace during a 5000-m race (r = 0.93), the marathon (r = 0.93) and a one-hour endurance run (r = 0.99). The striking correlation between V_d and running pace in the race indicates that V_d and AT are decisive factors for the pace in the race. During the one-hour run V_d and the pace in the race are almost equal. In the two other races, the 5000 m and the marathon, the values obtained (RP in the race) are different from V_d. The running pace in the 5000 m is faster than V_d; for the marathon it is the rverse. Here, runing pace is under V_d. These data are not surprising. In the 5000-m run the anaerobic system is constantly called upon, causing the running pace to be faster than V_d.

5000 m of the Los Angeles Olympics 1984

The share of the anaerobic system in a 5000-m race is, as far as energy is concerned, about 10%. Conconi's investigation points out that running pace in a 5000-m race is 3 to 9% faster than V_d (average 5.8%). In the marathon running pace is under the anaerobic threshold (AT), so also under V_d.

△ Speed skating race of one hour. Lactate around and above L 4.   ▽ Marathon race. Lactate 2.5 ± 0.5.

85

CONCONI'S TEST IN PRACTICE

Start with a warm-up of 15 to 20 minutes; then the proper test begins. The test person runs on a 400-m track. The pace at the start is slow. After every 200 meters running pace is increased. Every successive 200-m bit is run about 2 seconds faster. At the end of every 200 m pulse rate and running speed are registered. After every 200 m the athlete immediately accelerates and keeps his pace constant. The test goes on until the athlete cannot accelerate any more.

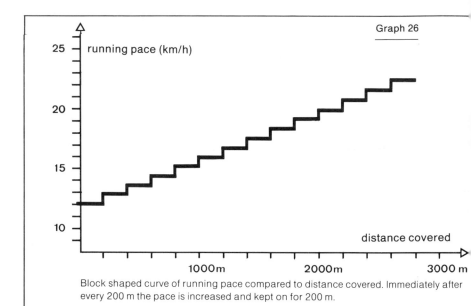

Block shaped curve of running pace compared to distance covered. Immediately after every 200 m the pace is increased and kept on for 200 m.

The test starts at point 1. At point 2 the athlete takes his PR and the helper standing at point one notes his time for every 200 m.
When returning to point 1 the athlete shouts the pulse rates of the first and the second 200-m bit. So at points 1 and 2 pulse rate and running time are taken down.

Starting pace
The pace chosen for the beginning depends on the condition of the athlete. Untrained persons run their first 200 m in 70 seconds; well-trained athletes, in 60 seconds. It is a rule of thumb that every successive 200 m is run 2 to 3 seconds faster; at the end of the test the 200-m pieces are run 1 to 2 seconds faster.

Equipment
The tools necessary for the test are a pulse monitor, a stopwatch, the protocol, a pen or pencil and a 400-m track.
N.B.: A helper will not be needed when a heart rate monitor with sufficient memory is used. By simply pressing the memory store button, pulse rate as well as running speed are registered.

Practical execution
The athlete starts at point 1. His helper is also standing there. At point 2 the athlete reads his PR. He then accelerates for the next 200 m. The helper clocks the 200 m times. When returning to point one, the athlete shouts the PRs of the

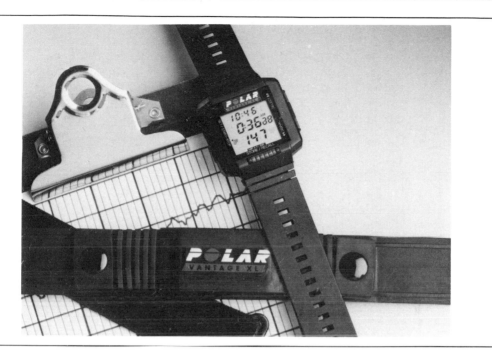

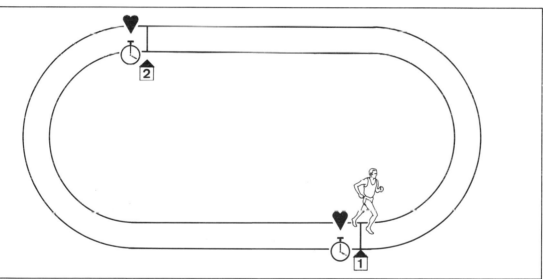

first and second 200 m; these PR values are registered by the helper. If the protocol is executed in this way the number of registrations is 12 to 16. The total running time is between 10 and 12 minutes, with a running distance between 2400 and 3200 m.

Working out the test data
The 200 m times are used to calculate the running pace in kilometers per hour (km/h).

The formula for this calculation is pace = 720/t.
t = running time per 200 m in seconds. In the table the pace can be read.

Place: . . . .   Date: . . . .
Name: . . . .   Age: . . . .
Sport: . . . .

Count	Distance	♥	⏱ Lap	km/h
1	200			
2	400			
3	600			
4	800			
5	1000			
6	1200			
7	1400			
8	1600			
9	1800			
10	2000			
11	2200			
12	2400			
13	2600			
14	2800			
15	3000			
16	3200			
17	3400			
18	3600			

time per 200 m	km per hour	time per 1000 m
sec. 70	10	6′00″
65	11	5′30″
60	12	5′00″
55	13	
	14	4′30″
50	15	4′00″
45	16	
	17	3′30″
40	18	
39		
38	19	
37		
36	20	3′00″
35		
34	21	
33	22	
32		
31	23	
30	24	2′30″
29	25	
28	26	
27		
	27	
26		
	28	
25	29	
24	30	2′00″

Protocol
Count: the number of 200-m bits covered.
Distance: the sum total of the distance.
Lap: 200 m times.

In the right-hand table the pace in km/h can be read when the time is known.

Example: 200 m time is 50 seconds. Running pace is 14.4 km/h in that case. The min./km bar gives the time per kilometer corresponding with that pace.

The results are drawn on graph paper.

The vertical, or Y-, axis is for PR.

The horizontal, or X-, axis is for pace in km/h.

The pulse rate and corresponding pace are put in. Pulse rate values under 120 are not registered. When all dots are put in, the curve is drawn. Some experience is required for finding the point of deflection. It might be helpful to know that the deflection point is mostly at a PR of 210 minus age. The deflection point corresponds with the anaerobic threshold. After the test it is known what PR or running pace corresponds to the anaerobic threshold.

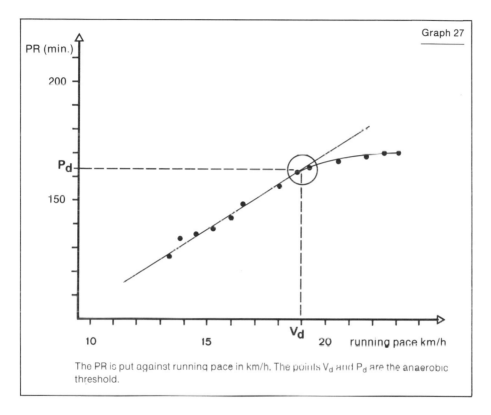

The PR is put against running pace in km/h. The points V_d and P_d are the anaerobic threshold.

The Conconi test gives information about the condition. On the basis of the test, training advice can be given and the effect of a training period can be established.

Rough information about condition

Condition	V_d km/h
Very bad	9.0
Bad	10.0
Acceptable	12.0
Excellent	14.0
Swiss marathon champion	19.0
World record marathon	23.6

Training advice

Here we distinguish between endurance runs in the aerobic range and intervals in the anaerobic range. The pace at V_d = 100% workload intensity.

Endurance run pace	intensity (%)	duration (min.)
slow	75	90 - 120
quiet	80	50 - 90
intermediate	90	30 - 30
fast	97	20 - 30
intervals		
long	100	6 - 12
short	103	3 - 6

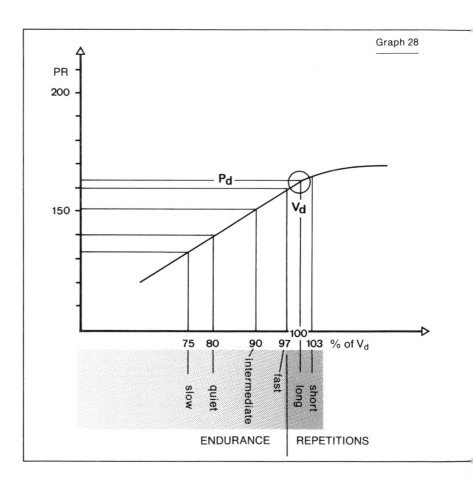

Graph 28

Training intensity can be expressed as a percentage of V_d. In the curve, pace and PR can be read for any given training intensity.

Effects of training

After a month of training the test can be repeated under equal circumstances. When endurance capacity is improved, the curve will move to the right. V_d will be faster then. If endurance capacity has gone down and V_d has become less fast, the curve will move to the left.

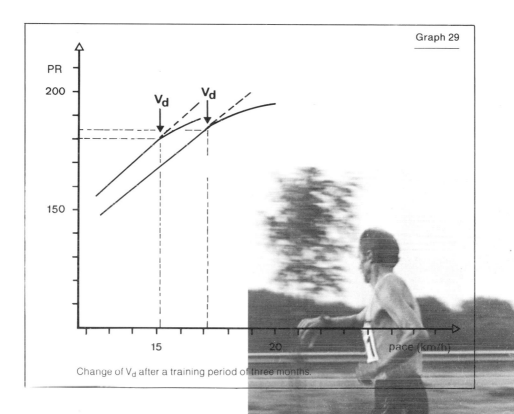

Change of V_d after a training period of three months.

Conconi's test only has sense when the athlete is capable of a maximum effort. His condition must be fairly good. An endurance run of 45 must be possible.

CONCONI'S TEST ADAPTED

In practice it takes some experience to run each 200 m piece about 2 seconds faster when you can only go by your own feeling. Therefore, the above test was made easier with the help of a prerecorded cassette tape.

Requirements for the test
– An athletics track with a clearly visible mark every 20 m.
– A table with precalculated times when, at the right pace, one of the marks must be passed.

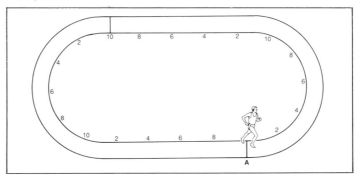

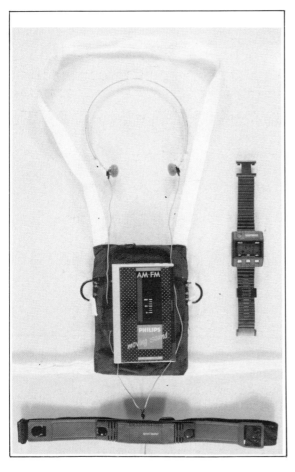

After every 200 m pace is accelerated 3 to 1 sec.							
mark/distance	time	mark/distance	time	mark/distance	time	mark/distance	time
2	6	2	3.47.5	2	6.48.4	2	9.18.4
4	12	4	3.52.4	4	6.52.4	4	9.21.8
6	18	6	3.57.3	6	6.56.5	6	9.25.2
8	24	8	4.02.2	8	7.00.5	8	9.28.6
10	30	10	4.07.1	10	7.04.5	10	9.32.0
2	36	2	4.11.9	2	7.08.5	2	9.35.3
4	42	4	4.16.8	4	7.12.5	4	9.38.7
6	48	6	4.21.7	6	7.16.6	6	9.42.1
8	54	8	4.26.6	8	7.20.6	8	9.45.5
10	60	10	4.31.5	10	7.24.6	10	9.48.9
2	1.05.7	2	4.36.2	2	7.28.4	2	9.52.2
4	1.11.4	4	4.40.8	4	7.32.3	4	9.55.4
6	1.17.1	6	4.45.5	6	7.36.1	6	9.58.7
8	1.22.8	8	4.50.1	8	7.40.0	8	10.02.0
10	1.28.5	10	4.54.8	10	7.43.8	10	10.05.3
2	1.34.2	2	4.59.4	2	7.47.6	2	10.08.5
4	1.39.9	4	5.04.1	4	7.51.5	4	10.11.8
6	1.45.6	6	5.08.7	6	7.55.3	6	10.15.1
8	1.51.3	8	5.13.4	8	7.59.2	8	10.18.3
400	1.57.0	1200	5.18.0	2000	8.03.0	2800	10.21.6
2	2.02.4	2	5.22.4	2	8.06.7	2	10.24.8
4	2.07.8	4	5.26.9	4	8.10.4	4	10.27.9
6	2.13.2	6	5.31.3	6	8.14.0	6	10.31.1
8	2.18.7	8	5.35.7	8	8.17.7	8	10.34.3
10	2.24.1	10	5.40.1	10	8.21.4	10	10.37.4
2	2.29.5	2	5.44.6	2	8.25.1	2	10.40.6
4	2.34.9	4	5.49.0	4	8.28.7	4	10.43.8
6	2.40.3	6	5.53.4	6	8.32.4	6	10.46.9
8	2.45.7	8	5.57.8	8	8.36.1	8	10.50.1
10	2.51.2	10	6.02.3	10	8.39.8	10	10.53.3
2	2.56.3	2	6.06.5	2	8.43.3	2	10.56.3
4	3.01.4	4	6.10.7	4	8.46.8	4	10.59.4
6	3.06.6	6	6.14.9	6	8.50.3	6	11.02.5
8	3.11.7	8	6.19.1	8	8.53.9	8	11.05.6
10	3.16.9	10	6.23.3	10	8.57.4	10	11.08.6
2	3.22.0	2	6.27.5	2	9.00.9	2	11.11.7
4	3.27.2	4	6.31.8	4	9.04.4	4	11.14.8
6	3.32.3	6	6.35.0	6	9.08.0	6	11.17.9
8	3.37.5	8	6.40.2	8	9.11.5	8	11.20.9
800	3.42.6	1600	6.44.4	2400	9.15.0	3200	11.24.0

– A light portable cassette player with headphones (see photo).
– A pouch or clip to fasten the cassette player.
– A cassette tape with the prerecorded text or signals when a mark should be passed, e.g., 2 - 4 - 6 - 8 etc. (can be made with the help of a simple recorder).
– A heart rate monitor with sufficient memory (Polar Sport Tester, Polar Vantage XL).
– Tables and graphs to work out test data.

Test data Conconi's test

Time	PR	Time	PR	Time	PR	Time	PR	Time	PR
0'00"	101	2'00"	137	4'00"	151	6'00"	164	8'00"	180
5"	107	5"	138	5"	150	5"	164	5"	180
10"	111	10"	139	10"	150	10"	166	10"	181
15"	112	15"	141	15"	151	15"	172	15"	182
20"	116	20"	143	20"	153	20"	170	20"	181
25"	121	25"	144	25"	153	25"	170	25"	180
30"	123	30"	144	30"	155	30"	169	30"	183
35"	124	35"	143	35"	155	35"	160	35"	184
40"	125	40"	143	40"	155	40"	170	40"	185
45"	126	45"	143	45"	154	45"	170	45"	188
50"	128	50"	142	50"	154	50"	172	50"	188
55"	129	55"	142	55"	156	55"	172	55"	185
1'00"	130	3'00"	142	5'00"	156	7'00"	172	9'00"	185
5"	132	5"	143	5"	155	5"	178	5"	186
10"	132	10"	143	10"	156	10"	175	10"	187
15"	131	15"	143	15"	156	15"	175	15"	187
20"	131	20"	144	20"	157	20"	175	20"	188
25"	131	25"	145	25"	158	25"	175	25"	188
30"	131	30"	146	30"	159	30"	177	30"	188
35"	132	35"	146	35"	162	35"	177	35"	188
40"	133	40"	146	40"	163	40"	177	40"	188
45"	136	45"	147	45"	164	45"	178	45"	188
50"	136	50"	148	50"	165	50"	178	50"	188
55"	137	55"	150	55"	166	55"	180	55"	188

Curve Conconi's test

Practical execution
Start with a warm-up of 15-20 min., then the proper test begins. The athlete runs on a 400-m track. The pace of the beginning is rather slow. Every successive 200-m stretch is run 3 to 1 sec. faster.

Pace at the beginning
Starting pace depends on the athlete's conditioning. Untrained athletes run the first 200 m in 70 sec.; well-trained persons in 60 sec. It is a rule of thumb that every successive 200 m is run 2 to 3 sec. faster, especially the first few 200-m stretches. At the end of the test every 200 m is run 1 to 2 sec. faster.

Beginning of the test
The athlete, equipped with cassette player and sport tester starts at A. He runs at a pace which is given to him through the headphones, until he is unable to reach the marks in time.
Check if everything is adjusted and in good order before the test. It is advisable to put on the sport tester during the warm-up to be sure it functions well.

Working out the test data

The 200 m times are rendered to running pace in kilometers per hour (km/h).
The formula is: pace $= 720/t$
t = running time per 200 m in seconds.

The results are graphed.
PR is put on the vertical, or Y-, axis. Pace in km/h is put on the horizontal, or X-, axis. Pulse rate and corresponding running pace are drawn up. PR values under 120 are not used.
When all dots are filled in, the curve is drawn. Finding the deflection is a matter of some experience. It might help to know that in many cases the deflection point is found near a PR of 210 minus the athlete's age. The deflection point is the anaerobic threshold. After the test this anaerobic threshold is a known factor.

No.	Distance	Pulse	200 m time	km/h	No	Distance	Pulse	200 m time	km/h
1	200	130	60,0	12,0	10	2000	180	38,4	18,75
2	400	137	57,0	12,6	11	2200	185	36,8	19,6
3	600	142	54,2	13,3	12	2400	187	35,3	20,4
4	800	146	51,5	14,0	13	2600	188	33,9	21,2
5	1000	155	48,9	14,7	14	2800		32,7	22,0
6	1200	157	46,5	15,5	15	3000		31,7	22,7
7	1400	164	44,3	16,3	16	3200		30,8	23,4
8	1600	170	42,2	17,1	17	3400			
9	1800	175	40,2	17,9	18	3600			

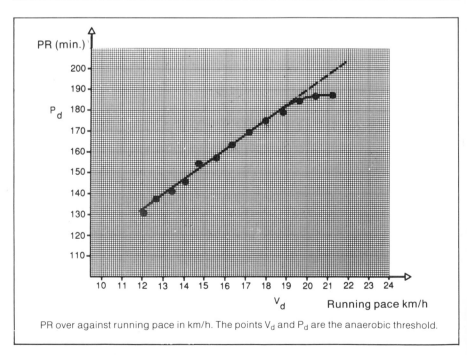

PR over against running pace in km/h. The points V_d and P_d are the anaerobic threshold.

(Research from Conconi's test adapted by Jan van den Bosch)

CONCONI'S TEST FOR CYCLISTS

Requirements for the test
A bicycle ergometer with a RPM meter and a meter for the number of watts (W) or newton-meters (Nm).
A table for calculating N into W.
A sport tester PE 3000.
Graph paper or a personal computer with a suitable program to work out the data.

Execution
After a warm-up of 10 minutes the test begins. The workload is increased by 10 to 15 watts every minute. The workload at the beginning of the test depends on the test person's condition. Less-trained cyclists start at 150 watts and well-trained at 200 watts.
PR is registered constantly
Pedaling frequency is kept at a constant level, e.g., 70 RPM; a higher frequency of 80 may also be possible, but always test the same person at the same pedaling frequency.
The test is ended when the test person cannot do the task any longer.

Working out the test data
The test data can be worked out on graph paper or with the help of a computer. See graph 30 and graph 31. The deflection point is clearly visible when a straight line is drawn over the values registered. At the deflection point the linear correlation between PR and W is lost.

Graph 30

Conconi's test on a poorly trained cyclist.
Onset workload 150 W.

– Pedaling frequency = 70 RPM.
– Total duration of the test is 20 min. including 10 min. warm-up.
– Maximum PR reached = 173.
– Maximum W = 286.
– PR at deflection point = 164.

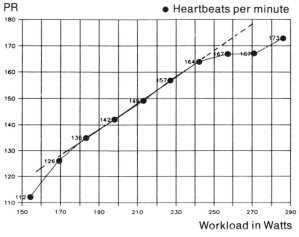

PR
● Heartbeats per minute
Workload in Watts

Test data L.Z. Test on 30 March 1988			
Min.	W	Nm	PR
11	154	21	112
12	169	23	126
13	183	25	135
14	198	27	142
15	213	29	149
16	227	31	157
17	242	33	164
18	257	35	167
19	271	37	167
20	286	39	173

Graph 31

Conconi's test on a well-trained cyclist.
Onset workload 180 W.

– Pedaling frequency = 70 RPM.
– Total duration of the test is 26 min.
  including 10 min. warm-up.
– Maximum PR reached = 168.
– Maximum W = 403.
– PR at deflection point = 160.

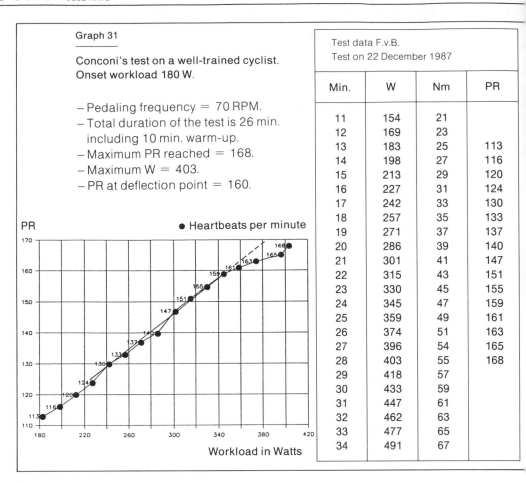

PR   ● Heartbeats per minute

Workload in Watts

Test data F.v.B.
Test on 22 December 1987

Min.	W	Nm	PR
11	154	21	
12	169	23	
13	183	25	113
14	198	27	116
15	213	29	120
16	227	31	124
17	242	33	130
18	257	35	133
19	271	37	137
20	286	39	140
21	301	41	147
22	315	43	151
23	330	45	155
24	345	47	159
25	359	49	161
26	374	51	163
27	396	54	165
28	403	55	168
29	418	57	
30	433	59	
31	447	61	
32	462	63	
33	477	65	
34	491	67	

This test is excellently suitable to establish changes in state of conditioning. Various tests can simply and quickly be compared, making changes in conditioning clearly visible.

Direct training advice can be given based on these data.

Top athletes from three different fields.
Three mountain kings in the Tour de France 1988: Gert-Jan Theunisse, Steven Rooks (the Netherlands) and Luis Herrera (Colombia).
Sprinter Ben Johnson (Canada).
World record holder triathlon Axel Koenders (the Netherlands) in Roth, W. Germany (8 hours 13 min.11).

DETERMINATION OF THE DEFLECTION POINT

The testing method

On the bicycle ergometer

Begin with a warm-up of 10 minutes. Then the load is increased every 5 minutes. After each period of 5 minutes, 2 ml of blood is taken and pulse rate is registered. The workload is a known factor.

The test person pedals without breaks, not even to take blood samples. The test is a maximum test. The athlete is taxed to his limits.

		PR	Watts	Lactate
Warm-up	10 minutes			
	15 minutes			
	20 minutes			
	25 minutes etc.			

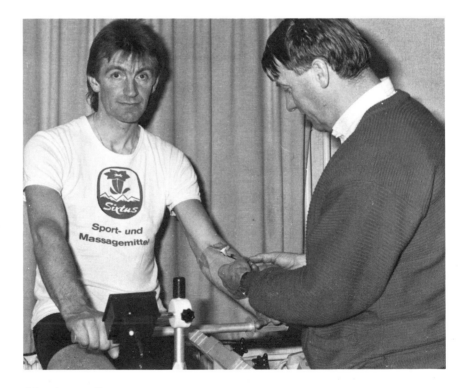

Blood sampling

Before the test a plastic tube is installed in vain in the arm. Such a plastic tube has some advantages. The test person has to be pricked only once. The test can be done without interruption. During the exertion, at any time necessary, blood can be taken without disturbing the test.

This blood is mixed in a tube with a test liquid. The blood is centrifuged within 4 hours. Blood cells and plasma are separated in this way. This plasma is stored in a separate tube. The plasma sample can be kept in a refrigerator for about one week. From this plasma sample lactate content is determined following Boehringer's method.

Field test

Warm-up of 10 minutes. Then certain distances are covered, e.g., running, cycling, cross-country skiing or swimming, with a duration of 5 minutes, starting with a low intensity. Every following period is covered faster. The pace is kept constant for 5 minutes and there is no final sprint. After every 5-minute period there is a 10-minute recovery break. The following data are registered: the time on the last 1000 m split (if this is known, the number of meters per second can easily be deduced) and the pulse rate at the end of each period; a 2 ml blood sample is taken.

Warm-up 10 min.	time 1000 m	m/sec.	PR	Lactate
1st 5-min. period				
10-min. recovery				
2nd 5-min. period				
10-min. recovery				
3rd 5-min. period				
10-min. recovery				
4th 5-min. period				

Equipment for ergometer test and field test

– bicycle ergometer
– sport tester
– blood sampling kit
– centrifuge
– coolbox to store and transport blood samples
– test protocol
– laboratory facilities for lactate determination
– for the field test: a track or route to follow.

In order to test reliably you must:

1. do the test under the same conditions and at the same time of day every day;
2. have no heavy meal for 5 hours before the test;
3. abstain from alcohol for 24 hours before the test;
4. have a good night's sleep;
5. abstain from coffee, tea or coca cola in the last hour before the test;
6. not train or do hard physical work on the day of the test;
7. see to it that you do not overexert yourself in training the day before the test;
8. always test at a constant temperature and air humidity;
9. do not test when you are ill or feverish;
10. do a good warm-up before every test.

In the laboratory

Determining the deflection point may be done in various ways. Mostly this determination takes place in the laboratory. During exertion tests the athletes are stressed with growing workloads. A blood sample is taken at fixed times for lactate determination. PR is registered during the complete test. With the help of the data obtained, it is simple to draw the graph showing the relation between PR and lactate content.

Curve 18
Registration of a laboratory test on a bicycle ergometer.

Registration of an exertion test with growing workload. Just before the workload is increased a blood sample is taken for lactate determination. The PR (pulse rate) is taken constantly. Below in the curve are PR (pulse rate) and L (lactate content), which correspond to each other.

The data from curve 16 are worked out in a pulse rate/lactate graph (see graph 32; in this graph PR and its corresponding lactate content can easily be read).

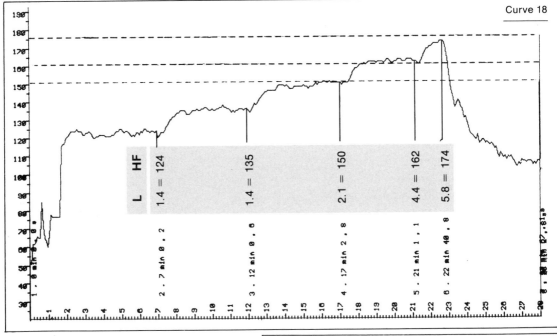

Curve 18

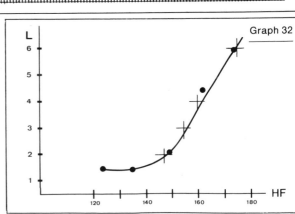

Graph 32

From the graph it follows:
L 2 = 147
L 3 = 155
L 4 = 160
L 6 = 175

100

During physical exercise

Determining the deflection point can also take place during physical exercise. This may be a great advantage. Then the athlete is tested in a sport-specific manner.

For example: testing a marathon runner on a bicycle ergometer supplies you with results which cannot be used as a basis for advice on running training. A marathon runner should have a sport-specific test, i.e., while running.

Curve 19
Lactate determination in a marathon runner under sport-specific conditions.
The test person is tested while running on the road, 4 x 1 km, with a recovery break. Every successive kilometer is run faster. After every kilometer a blood sample is taken. High in the curve the PR and corresponding lactate content are stated.

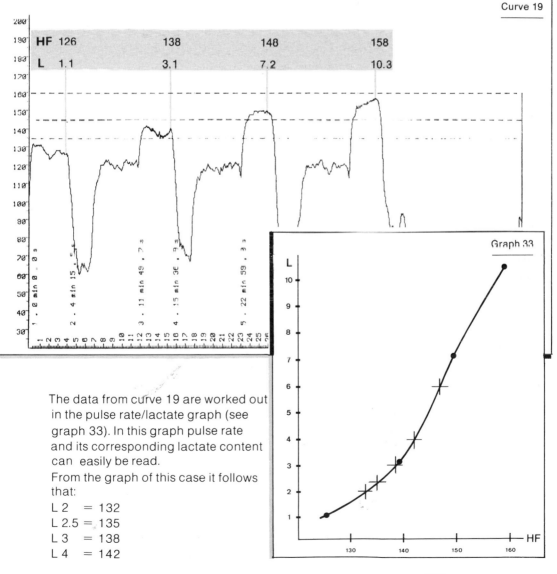

Curve 19

| HF | 126 | 138 | 148 | 158 |
| L | 1.1 | 3.1 | 7.2 | 10.3 |

Graph 33

The data from curve 19 are worked out in the pulse rate/lactate graph (see graph 33). In this graph pulse rate and its corresponding lactate content can easily be read.

From the graph of this case it follows that:

L 2 = 132
L 2.5 = 135
L 3 = 138
L 4 = 142

*Another example of determining the deflection point during physical
exercise.*

Curve 20
After an extensive warm-up the athlete runs 3 periods of about 10 minutes each.
Every period is run faster but at a constant pace. After every period of exertion
blood is taken immediately for lactate determination. In between the fast periods
there is a recovery period, long enough to have the lactic acid be broken down.
The test data are as follows:

PR 135 = L   1.9
PR 145 = L   4.7
PR 155 = L 11.2

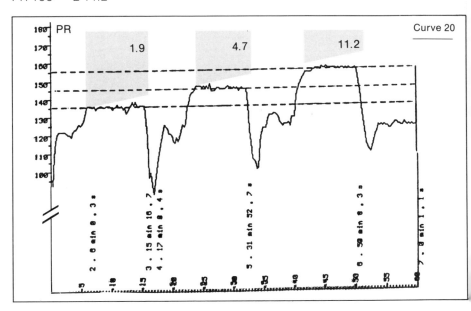

These data suffice to create the right lactate/PR graph. The advantage of such
measuring is that the athlete is tested during a normal workout; so there is no
loss of training hours because the test itself may be considered a good training
workout.

Determining the deflection point without measuring lactate

The athlete performs during at least 30 minutes as intensely as possible. This
effort must be done at a constant level. Loss of pace must not be allowed. The
PR at which this effort is performed often corresponds rather well with the
deflection point.

Curve 21
Maximum, constant exertion during 60 minutes.
Bicycling training on the road during 60 minutes at a level high pace. The
average PR is 160. The deflection point, expected for this athlete, was about
160. This curve comes from the same person as curve 18.
In the laboratory test the deflection point was also 160.
This road test gives the same deflection point as the bicycle ergometer test.

102

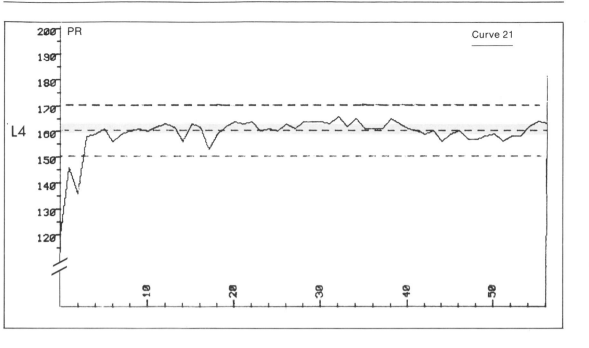

American pro cyclist Andy Bishop during a time trial of well over one hour. The exertion is around and above the deflection.

Determining the deflection point without measuring lactate, derived from maximum PR for cyclists

If you cannot avail yourself of possibilities to have a lactate performance curve drawn up, the maximum PR supplies you with a lot of information.

It is of vital importance though, to *determine PR* **exactly** and in a well-rested state.

Starting from maximum PR, the various training levels can rather accurately be indicated (see table).

This table applies only to well-trained endurance cyclists.

Determination of maximum PR

Maximum PR can only be determined when you are well recovered. The determination is as follows: a warm-up ride of about 15 minutes is followed by an intensive time trial of 10 minutes. The last minute is ridden maximally; the last 20 to 30 seconds are sprinted. Now the maximum pulse rate can simply be read on the pulse rate monitor.

Do not rely on one single determination for establishing your maximum PR. Various attempts, preferably also in racing conditions, are necessary to determine the exact maximum PR.

Lactate values derived from maximum pulse rates for cyclists

max. PR	L 4	L 3	L 2.5	L 2	max. PR	L 4	L 3	L 2.5	L 2
150	137	133	129	124	180	165	159	155	149
151	138	133	130	125	181	166	160	155	150
152	139	134	131	126	182	167	161	156	150
153	140	135	131	127	183	168	162	157	151
154	141	136	132	127	184	168	163	158	152
155	142	137	133	128	185	169	163	159	153
156	143	138	134	129	186	170	164	160	154
157	144	139	135	130	187	171	165	161	155
158	145	140	136	131	188	172	166	161	155
159	146	140	137	131	189	173	167	162	156
160	147	141	137	132	190	174	168	163	157
161	147	142	138	133	191	175	169	164	158
162	148	143	139	134	192	176	170	165	159
163	149	144	140	135	193	177	171	166	160
164	150	145	141	136	194	178	171	167	160
165	151	146	142	136	195	179	172	167	161
166	152	147	143	137	196	179	173	168	162
167	153	148	143	138	197	180	174	169	163
168	154	148	144	139	198	181	175	170	164
169	155	149	145	140	199	182	176	171	165
170	156	150	146	141	200	183	177	172	165
171	157	151	147	141	201	184	178	173	166
172	158	152	148	142	202	185	178	173	167
173	158	153	149	143	203	186	179	174	168
174	159	154	149	144	204	187	180	175	169
175	160	155	150	145	205	188	181	176	170
176	161	156	151	146	206	189	182	177	170
177	162	156	152	146	207	190	183	178	171
178	163	157	153	147	208	190	184	179	172
179	164	158	154	148	209	191	185	179	173

L1 → 142 b/s.

COACHING A MARATHON RUNNER WITH THE HELP OF PR REGISTRATION AND LACTATE MEASURING

The Helmond Marathon (1985)

Name: F.P.
Age: 42
Weight: 61.2 kg (135 lb.)
Height: 171.2 cm (5′7″).

Running history: since years about 3 marathons a year. Personal best: 2.40.09 (1979); 2.43; 2.45; 2.50; 2.58; 3.01.
Maximum distance a week: about 120 km (75 miles).

Question: The athlete asks for help on 21st of August 1985, requesting coaching for the Helmond marathon on 21st of October 1985. He has just recovered from an Achilles tendon injury. He ran his best in 1979. Since then every marathon has failed. After 30-35 km he is burnt out, empty, muscles do not obey any more.

Coaching
Pulse rate registration and lactate measuring.

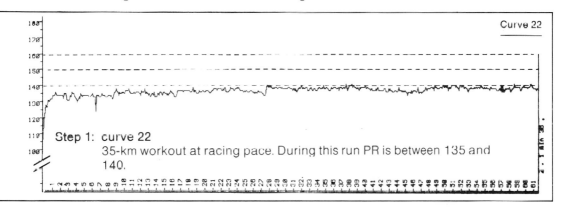

Step 1: curve 22
   35-km workout at racing pace. During this run PR is between 135 and 140.

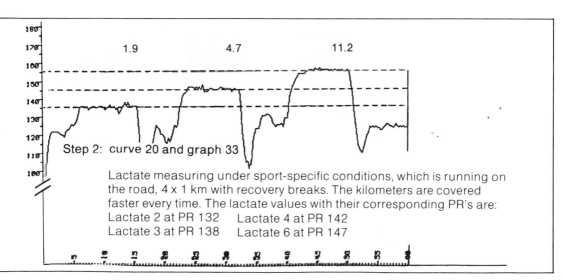

Step 2: curve 20 and graph 33
   Lactate measuring under sport-specific conditions, which is running on the road, 4 x 1 km with recovery breaks. The kilometers are covered faster every time. The lactate values with their corresponding PR's are:
   Lactate 2 at PR 132   Lactate 4 at PR 142
   Lactate 3 at PR 138   Lactate 6 at PR 147

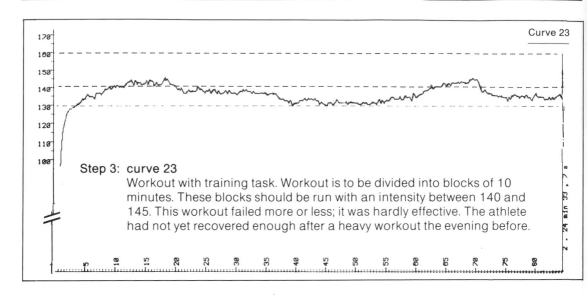

Step 3: curve 23
Workout with training task. Workout is to be divided into blocks of 10 minutes. These blocks should be run with an intensity between 140 and 145. This workout failed more or less; it was hardly effective. The athlete had not yet recovered enough after a heavy workout the evening before.

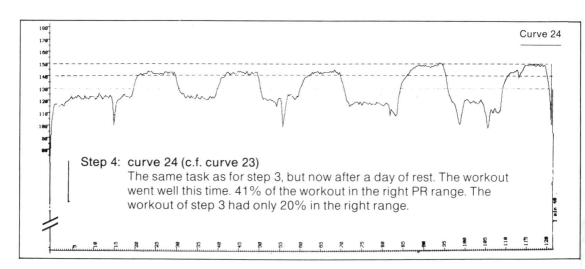

Step 4: curve 24 (c.f. curve 23)
The same task as for step 3, but now after a day of rest. The workout went well this time. 41% of the workout in the right PR range. The workout of step 3 had only 20% in the right range.

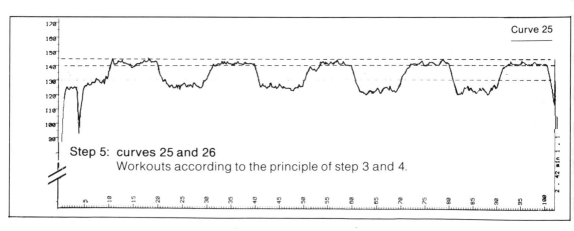

Step 5: curves 25 and 26
Workouts according to the principle of step 3 and 4.

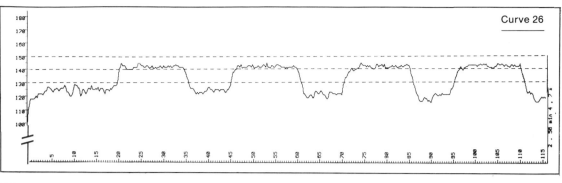

Curve 26

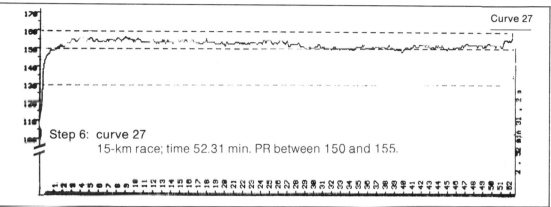

Curve 27

Step 6: curve 27
15-km race; time 52.31 min. PR between 150 and 155.

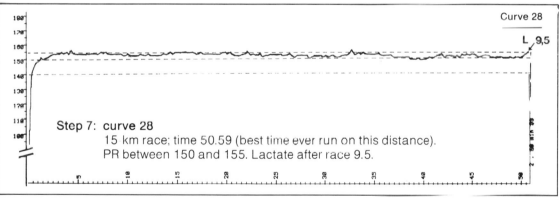

Curve 28

L 9,5

Step 7: curve 28
15 km race; time 50.59 (best time ever run on this distance).
PR between 150 and 155. Lactate after race 9.5.

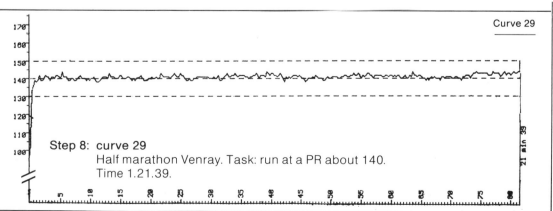

Curve 29

Step 8: curve 29
Half marathon Venray. Task: run at a PR about 140.
Time 1.21.39.

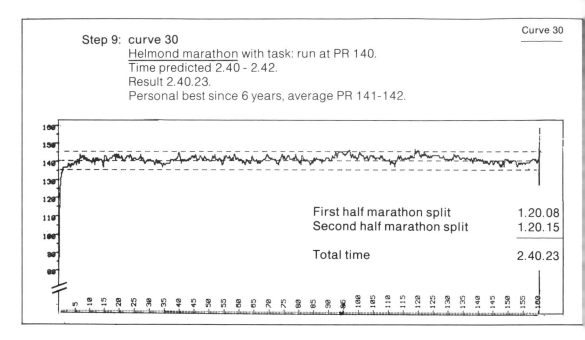

Curve 30

Step 9: curve 30
Helmond marathon with task: run at PR 140.
Time predicted 2.40 - 2.42.
Result 2.40.23.
Personal best since 6 years, average PR 141-142.

First half marathon split	1.20.08
Second half marathon split	1.20.15
Total time	2.40.23

Summary:
The athlete was advised to train in blocks of intensive endurance intervals. PR during these workouts was between 140 and 145. The lactate test on the road showed that L 3 and L 4 correspond with PR 138 and PR 142, respectively. Because of the recent Achilles tendon injury, the endurance workouts were set at faster levels. Once a week the athlete ran a 15-km race at a PR well above the deflection point (PR 150-155). This is also proved by the lactate registration of 9.5 (see curve 28).
These races are a good training of the anaerobic capacity (lactate tolerance training). A marathon cannot be run at this intensity. From the registration it appears that there is practically no loss of pace. The combination of 3 x a week an intensive endurance workout, 2 x a week a recovery run and 1 x a week a lactate tolerance workout has turned out to be the ideal preparation for this athlete.

The Westland Marathon

Coaching the same marathon runner was taken in hand again for the preparation for the Westland marathon of 12 April 1986. The specific training was started in January 1986. Preparation time was considerably longer than for the Helmond marathon, which was in October 1985. On account of the success of the previous way of coaching we chose for the same principle: three times a week endurance workouts, mostly in blocks with a PR about the deflection point. Once a week a race or training workout well above the deflection point. The day after a heavy workout or race a low intensity run: the so-called recovery workout. For this athlete 3 x a week endurance workout and 1 x a week a lactate tolerance workout is the ideal mix for an optimum preparation. In the period between October and January the athlete trained in a quiet and relaxed manner, participating in a cross-country race when he felt like it.

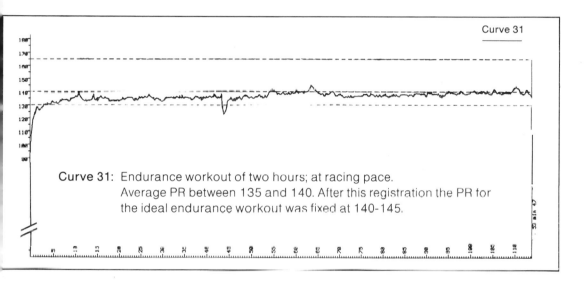

Curve 31: Endurance workout of two hours; at racing pace.
Average PR between 135 and 140. After this registration the PR for the ideal endurance workout was fixed at 140-145.

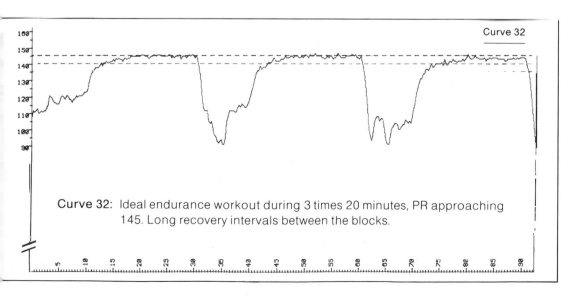

Curve 32: Ideal endurance workout during 3 times 20 minutes, PR approaching 145. Long recovery intervals between the blocks.

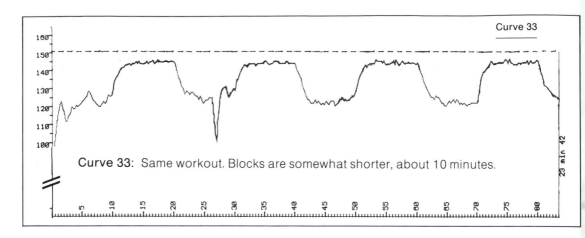

Curve 33: Same workout. Blocks are somewhat shorter, about 10 minutes.

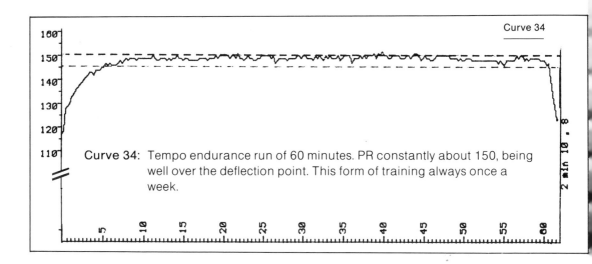

Curve 34: Tempo endurance run of 60 minutes. PR constantly about 150, being well over the deflection point. This form of training always once a week.

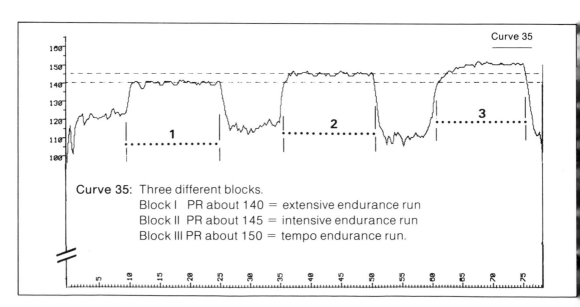

Curve 35: Three different blocks.
Block I   PR about 140 = extensive endurance run
Block II PR about 145 = intensive endurance run
Block III PR about 150 = tempo endurance run.

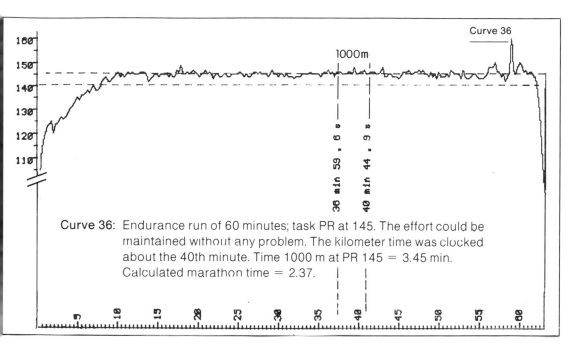

Curve 36: Endurance run of 60 minutes; task PR at 145. The effort could be maintained without any problem. The kilometer time was clocked about the 40th minute. Time 1000 m at PR 145 = 3.45 min. Calculated marathon time = 2.37.

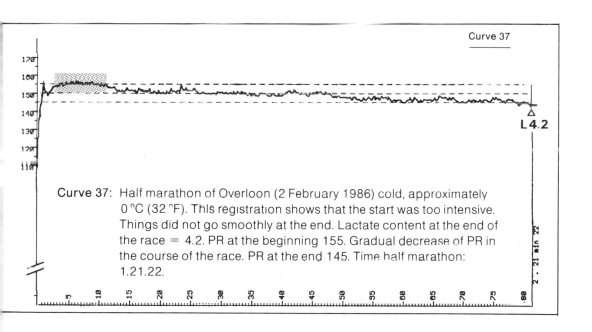

Curve 37: Half marathon of Overloon (2 February 1986) cold, approximately 0 °C (32 °F). This registration shows that the start was too intensive. Things did not go smoothly at the end. Lactate content at the end of the race = 4.2. PR at the beginning 155. Gradual decrease of PR in the course of the race. PR at the end 145. Time half marathon: 1.21.22.

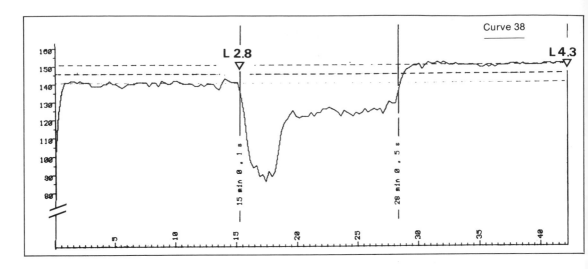

Curve 38: Lactate test on the road during sport-specific test. Task: run 15 minutes at PR 140. Then long recovery break, then run 15 minutes at PR 150.
After 15 minutes of running at PR 140, lactate content is 2.8.
After 15 minutes of running at PR 150, lactate content is 4.3
The following values can now be calculated.
Lactate 2 corresponds with PR 135
Lactate 3 corresponds with PR 142
Lactate 4 corresponds with PR 147/148.

Conclusion:

The deflection point compared to the Helmond marathon has shifted from PR 142 to PR 147/148.

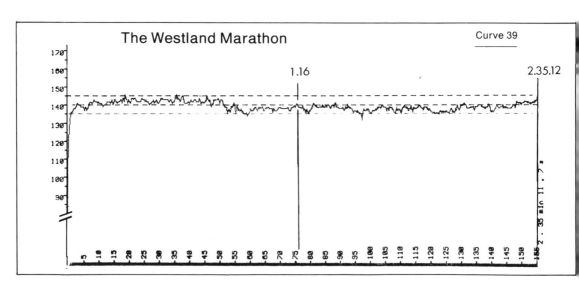

Curve 39: **Westland marathon** on 12 April 1986.

Weather conditions: cold weather, 4-5 °C, much wind. Race task: run at a pace corresponding with a PR of 140-145 beats per minute.

During the race the athlete runs the first 50 minutes accordingly. At that moment he joins a group of 25 runners. Because the time expected is well under shedule (target time is 2.37) his coach who accompanies him on a bicycle, advises him to stick to this group. In the shelter of this group PR clearly drops. This indicates how important the role of a so-called 'hare' may be.

The half marathon is run in 1.16 h. The second part in 1.19.12. Total time 2.35.12 h.

The athlete has not had any problem at all during the complete marathon. He had the feeling that he could keep up the pace of the first 50 minutes 'easily'. The total time means improving his personal best by more than 5 minutes. After the marathon a rapid and good recovery.

We expect that more progress must be possible. A total time of 2.30 does not seem impossible.

FIELD TEST AND TRAINING ADVICE FOR MARATHON RUNNERS OF INTERNATIONAL AND INTERMEDIATE LEVEL

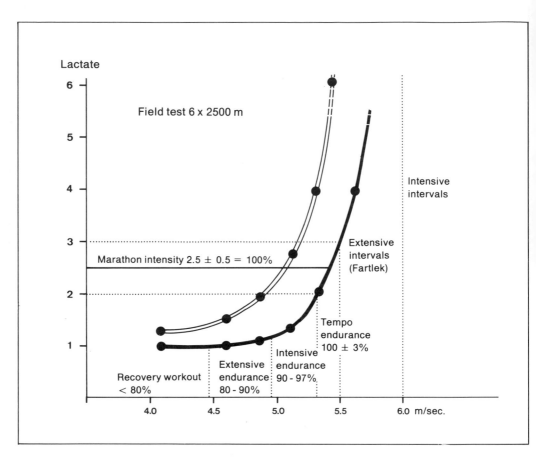

The right-hand curve is the average lactate curve of marathon runners of *international level.* They run an ideal marathon with an intensity corresponding to 2.5 ± 0.5 lactate. This intensity is set at 100%.
The various training intensities are deduced from it.

The left-hand curve is that of *well-trained* marathoners. Their optimum marathon intensity is at lactate 3.0 ± 0.5.

Source: Deutsche Zeitschrift für Sportmedizin, Heft 1/1985, Trainingssteuerung im Hochleistungssport: einige Aspekte und Beispiele. Von Liesen u.a., p. 8-18.

TWO REGISTRATIONS OF A MARATHON RUNNER

Curve Eindhoven marathon. October 1985

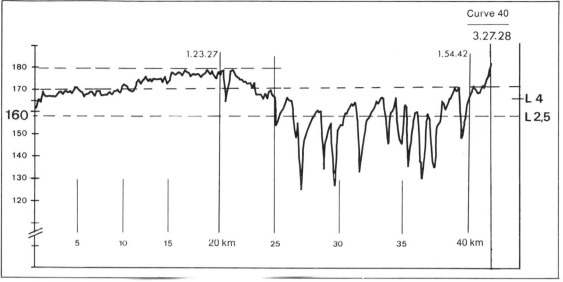

From the start to the 25th kilometer PR is over 165. So this runner can perform about 1 hour and 50 minutes over his deflection point. Then he cannot keep up his pace any longer. Running speed goes down rapidly. So does his PR. The first 20 km split is covered in 1.23.27 and the second in 1.54.42.
Total time marathon: 3 h. 27 min. 28 sec.

Conclusion: A classical example of a failed marathon.
On the basis of test data, training was adapted (test April) and the correct race-intensity was determined (test September).

Test data:	
April 1987	September 1987
Lactate 2 = PR 155	Lactate 2 = PR 156
Lactate 3 = PR 160	Lactate 3 = PR 161
Lactate 4 = PR 165	Lactate 4 = PR 165
V 2 = 3.64 meters/sec.	V 2 = 4.00 meters/sec.
V 3 = 3.78 meters/sec.	V 3 = 4.10 meters/sec.
V 4 = 3.95 meters/sec.	V 4 = 4.19 meters/sec.
V 2.5 = 3 hours 9 minutes	V 2.5 = 2 hours 53 minutes

These test data show that PR levels have not changed between April and September, whereas his performance capacity has strongly increased. The marathon time calculated with a running pace at lactate 2.5 (V 2.5) has improved from 3 h. 9 min. to 2 h. 53 min.

Curve Helmond marathon. October 1986

A prudent start. He kept his PR at the beginning of the race constantly under

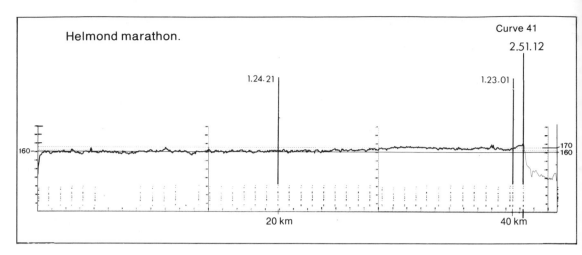

160. Later in the race PR between 160-165, from two hours PR between 165 and 170.
1st 20-km split 1.24.21
2nd 20-km split 1.23.01 (a so-called positive split).
Total time marathon 2 h. 51 min. 12.7 sec.
Personal best. For the first time he ran under 3 hours.
At the beginning of the race he has willingly and knowingly kept himself under control.

Conclusion: well-controlled, good marathon race.

CONCISE EXAMPLE OF A LACTATE TEST AND SPORT ADVICE FOR A CYCLIST

First of all a registration was made of an intensive endurance workout on the road. The task was to cycle at a maximum pace for 60 minutes without loss of speed. From the registration of as long as 90 minutes PR turns out to fluctuate constantly between 160 and 165. If the intensity of this effort has been high enough, the deflection point will be in the PR range between 160 and 165. The cyclist says that he has performed constantly against his maximum.

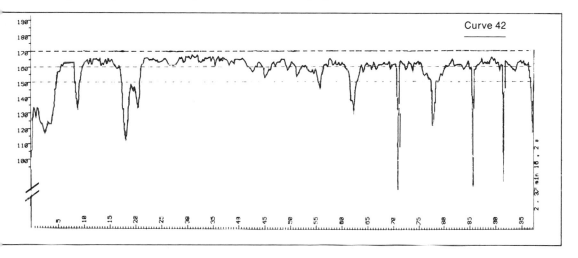

Curve 42

From the lactate test on the bicycle ergometer, two days after the test on the road, we obtained the following information (see graph 34).

Lactate 2 = 145 PR
Lactate 3 = 157 PR
Lactate 4 = 164 PR (deflection point)
Lactate 5 = 173 PR.

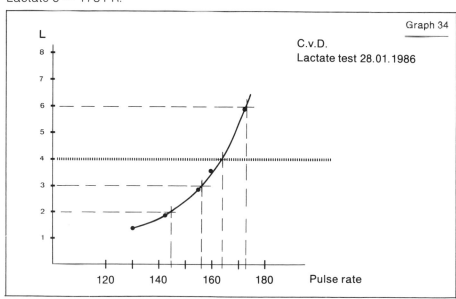

Graph 34

C.v.D.
Lactate test 28.01.1986

117

The first conclusion is that the test on the road, during which no lactate measuring took place, points out fairly well where the deflection point is; the test on the road and the laboratory test correspond well. In the two tests the deflection point is between 160 and 165 PR.
As for training workouts this implies the following advice:
Recovery workout: PR not over 130-140
Extensive endurance: PR between 140 and 155
Intensive endurance: PR between 155 and 165
Intensity training (intervals): PR over 165.

Training coach and cyclist were advised for a good mix in relation to the racing program.

PRACTICAL EXAMPLE OF A LACTATE TEST AND TRAINING ADVICE FOR A PRO CYCLIST

Ergometer test: J. Draayer, pro cyclist PDM team
Body weight = 75.8 kg (167 lb.)
11.03.1988

Execution of the test:

After a warm-up of 6 minutes, the workload is increased every five minutes.
During the test PR is continually registered. At the end of every exercise period
blood is sampled for lactate determination.

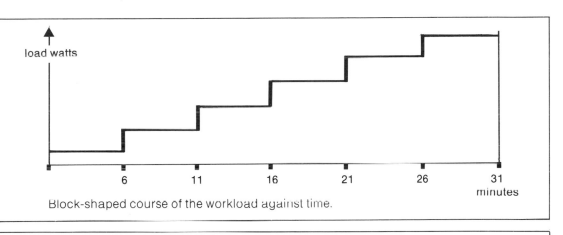

Block-shaped course of the workload against time.

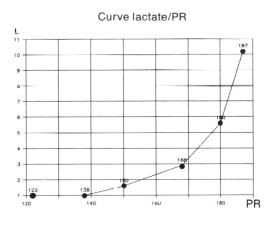

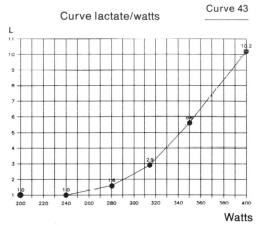

Curve 43

Test results

L	PR	Watts
1.0	122	200
1.0	138	240
1.6	150	280
2.9	167	315
5.6	180	350
10.2	187	400

PR maximum: 187
Maximum lactate: 10.2
Continuation time at 400 watts
(maximum) = 3 min. 23 sec.

Values
deduced

L	PR		Watts	Watts per kg bodyweight	% Watts maximum
2.0	155 =	83% PR max.	291	3.84	72.8%
2.5	162 =	87% PR max.	304	4.01	
3.0	167 =	89% PR max.	316	4.17	
4.0	172 =	92% PR max.	329	4.34	82.3%
10.2	187 =	100% PR max.	400	5.28	

TRAINING ADVICE

On the basis of the lactate/PR curve the following training advice is given:

Training intensities:

Recovery ride: PR under 140
This workout should be done the day after a strenuous race or workout, when you have not yet completely recovered.

Training endurance capacity:
Level 1: 'quiet'   =   PR 140 - 150
Level 2: intermediate   =   PR 150 - 160
Level 3: intensive   =   PR 160 - 170

The larger part of your training (± 80-90%) should be endurance exercise. As for intensity to be divided as follows:
60% at level 1
30% at level 2
10% at level 3.

Training lactate tolerance: PR over 170
A) short – duration 20 to 180 seconds
            – recovery pause 1 to 2 minutes
            – intensity: high. Above 92% and to 95% of the PR max. = PR 172 - 177
            – number of intervals: starting with 5 x, gradually going up to 10 - 15 - 20 x
            – do this workout only when you have fully recuperated.

B) long – duration 3 to 10 minutes
            – recovery pause 5 to 10 minutes
            – intensity: high. 90% to 92% PR max. = PR 168 - 172
            – number: starting with 3 x, gradually going up to 4 or 5 x.

Do not overdo the lactate tolerance workouts. Once or twice a week (including races) is more than enough.

Sprint workouts:
duration : short 10 to 20 seconds
recovery : long   2 to 5 minutes
intensity : high: 95 to 100%. The max. PR cannot be reached because the time is too short
number   : starting with 3 x, gradually going up to 10 x.

Power training:
duration : long 3 to 5 minutes
recovery : long 5 to 10 minutes
intensity : intermediately intensive. 85% to 90% of the PR maximum = PR 160 - 170
number   : starting with 3 x, gradually going up to 10 x.

Do this workout with a heavy gear, low pedaling frequency riding uphill or in a front wind; remain sitting on the saddle.

EXTENSIVE EXAMPLE OF A FIELD TEST AND TRAINING ADVICE FOR A MARATHON RUNNER

Sportmedische praktijk Deurne
Peter Janssen, arts
Deltasingel 29
5751 SL DEURNE
Tel. 04930 - 16828

Lactaattest

Date test:	25.09.1986		Weather conditions:	dry
Time:	afternoon		Temperature:	16 ºC
Place of test:	Deurne-road		Air humidity:	high
Form of test:	3 x 10 min.		Wind force:	calm
Executed by:	P.J.			
Name:	C.B.		Training coach:	unknown
Date of birth:	19.09.1959		Address:	–
Address:	–		Place:	–
Place:	Venray			
Sport:	running 10 km – marathon		Particulars:	none

Test data

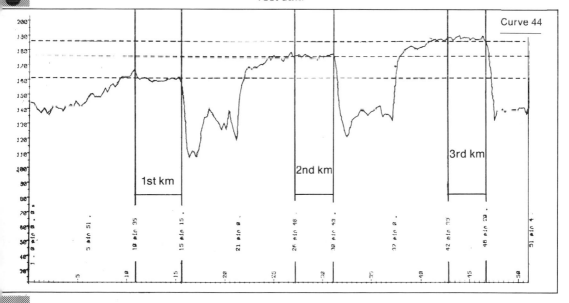

	Time: min.sec.	PR	Lactate	Speed: m/sec.
1st km	4.44	160	1.1	3.52
2nd km	4.01	175	3.1	4.15
3rd km	3.48	187	10.0	4.39

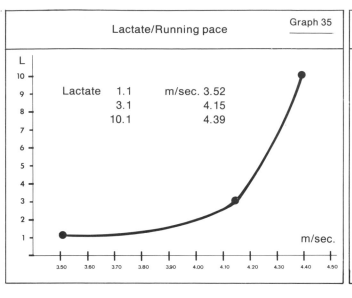

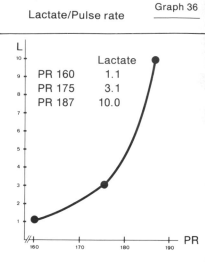

Data deduced

Speed/ lactate	speed m/sec.	speed km/h	km time min.sec.	marathon time	Lactate	Pulse rate
V 2*	3.83	13.79	4.24		2	167
V 2.5	3.98	14.33	4.12	2.56.42	3	175
V 3	4.11	14.90	4.00		4	180
V 4	4.25	15.30	3.54		6	185
V 5	4.29	15.44	3.52			
V 6	4.32	15.55	3.50			
V 8	4.36	15.69	3.48			
V 10	4.40	15.84	3.44			

* V 2: running pace at lactate 2

TRAINING ADVICE

Endurance workouts

Training endurance capacity can best be done at lactate values between 2 and 4 millimoles. The quiet or extensive endurance workout between 2 and 3 mM lactate. The intensive endurance workout between 3 and 4 mM lactate. These values are valid for most athletes.

Not very well-trained persons train their endurance capacity at somewhat higher lactate values:
intensive 4.- 5/6 mM lactate
extensive 3 - 4 mM lactate.
Very well-trained athletes train their endurance capacity at somewhat lower lactate values:
extensive 1.5 - 2.5 mM lactate
intensive 2.5 - 3.5 mM lactate.

The intensity with which a marathon is run corresponds with a lactate content of 2.5 mM ± 0.5.
Your marathon time at V 2.5 is 2 hours 56 min. and 42 sec.

122

In an *endurance workout* lactate content must not rise too high. If during workouts too high lactic contents arise *lactate tolerance* is trained instead of endurance capacity.
Intensive workouts going together with high lactate values may be damaging to endurance capacity. *Endurance capacity may deteriorate by this kind of training.*

Proposition for an endurance workout:
The workout is to be divided in blocks of 10 - 15 - 20 minutes of exertion, followed by recovery breaks of 5 - 10 minutes.

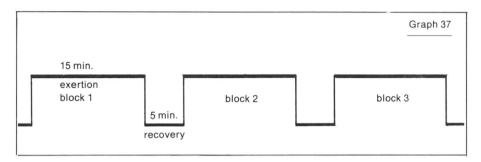

Graph 37

Extensive endurance	Intensive endurance	Combination extensive and intensive
Intensity between L 2 - L 3 V 2 - V 3 PR 170 - PR 175	Intensity between L 3 - L 4 V 3 - V 4 PR 175 - PR 180	Block 1 extensive Recovery Block 2 Intensive Recovery Block 3 extensive etc.

These workouts form the basis for developing and keeping up endurance capacity. Other combinations, as stated above, are possible such as larger blocks, less recovery.
If after due time endurance capacity has increased, pace must be set again.

Lactate tolerance training

During this form of training lactate values over 4 mM arise. Values as much as 10 mM lactate are often reached. This kind of workout should not be done too often by a marathon runner. Two forms of tolerance training are important to a marathoner.

A. *Tempo runs:* e.g., 1000-m running.
E.g., 5 x 1 km with a pace over V 4. Times between 3.45 min and 3.55 min. with PR over 180.
Do not take too long recovery breaks; after all, high lactate values are meant to be built up. When there is too much recovery, lactate content goes down. Start with 3 x 1 km and slowly go to, e.g., 10 x 1 km. The number you plan to do must be done without loss of pace. If you are exhausted after 3 x 1 km and the task was 6 x 1 km, you started too fiercely.

B. *Run*, preferably in a race, 10 to 15 km at a pace or a PR just over the deflection point, so over V 4 or over PR 180. During these races lactate content gradually goes up to 8 - 10 - 12 mM.

It is impossible to complete a marathon at this pace. Take care: do not do these workouts A and B, too often.

Recovery runs

The day after a heavy workout or race you should always do a recovery run. The recovery run is done under V 2 or under the pulse rate related to lactate 2, so V 2 is slower than 4 minutes and 24 seconds per km. PR well under 170.

SUMMARY

☐ *Endurance training:*

Pace	Pulse rate
V 2 - V 4 = 4.24 - 3.54	L 2 - L 4 = 170 - 180
Extensive V 2 - V 3 = 4.24 - 4.00	Extensive L 2 - L 3 = 170 - 175
Intensive V 3 - V 4 = 4.00 - 3.54	Intensive L 3 - L 4 = 175 - 180

These workouts should be done in blocks.
Number 3 to 4 times a week.

☐ *Lactate tolerance training:*

A. Tempo runs, e.g., 1000 m runs with recovery breaks.
1000 m at a pace higher than V 4 = 3.45 - 3.55.
Number at the beginning 3 x, gradually going up to 10 x.
Recovery breaks 2 to 3 minutes.
B. Race of about 50 minutes, e.g., 15 km run at a pace higer than V 4.

EXTENSIVE EXAMPLE OF TRAINING ADVICE FOR A GIRL SWIMMER

Sportmedische praktijk Deurne
Peter Janssen, arts
Deltasingel 29
5751 SL DEURNE
Tel. 04930 - 16828

Date	04.11.1986	Sport:	swimming
		Category:	races
Female:	14 years old	Union:	KNZB
Name:	van der AA	Test place:	pool, Gemert
First name:	Ellen	Test form:	4 x 300-m front crawl
Date of birth:			100-m sprint
Address:		Time:	evening
Place:	Gemert		
Postal code:			
Tel. number:			

Particulars: No progress in last 18 months, despite many intensive workouts. Training intensity has probably always been too high.

Test target: Setting the right training intensity.

Personal bests: 1985: 100 m: 1.02.3 min., 200 m: 2.15.9 min., 400 m: 4.38
1986: 100 m: 1.05.5 min., 200 m: 2.18

Test:

10 minutes warm-up

	time	m/sec.	m/min.	lactate
300 m	' 5.01	0.99	59.80	1.7
recovery 5 min.				
300 m	4.01	1.24	74.68	5.2
recovery 5 min.				
300 m	3.48	1.32	78.95	8.4
recovery 10 min.				
300 m	3.40	1.36	81.81	9.6
recovery 10 min.				
100 m	1.05	1.54	93.31	13.9

Data deduced:

Lactate 2 = 1.16 m/sec. = V 2
Lactate 3 = 1.18 m/sec. = V 3
Lactate 4 = 1.21 m/sec. = V 4
Lactate 5 = 1.23 m/sec. = V 5
Lactate 6 = 1.27 m/sec. = V 6

The test was a complete success. The three dots higher than lactate 4 are in a straight line.
The V 4 is 1.21 m/sec.
The German national level: V 4 is between 1.20 and 1.30 m/sec.
The European level: V 4 is between 1.40 and 1.50 m/sec.
The world and Olympic level: V 4 is between 1.50 and 1.67 m/sec.

So your V 4 pace is not bad at all. During the test you surpass lactate 4 very fast. After the second 300 m lactate has gone up to 5.2 mM/liter. The supposition that your training intensity has often been too high is confirmed by these data.

TRAINING ADVICE

Swim 400 m a number of times at your V 4 pace. This 400 m is in 5.31 min. You are supposed to get to know the feeling of swimming with a lactate content of 4. Have your split times checked and recorded, enabling you to check whether you swim constantly. So get to know the V 4 feeling. 400 m times between 5.26 and 5.34.

A. *Recovery swims* at lactate 2 or even less intensive.

B. Do not do races or *lactate tolerance workouts* more often than once a week; then lactate content goes up to high values, as high as 8 and more.
During your 100-m sprint you build up a lactate content of 13.9.
The day after a heavy race or workout you should always do a recovery or regeneration swim.

C. You train *endurance capacity* at L 2, L 3, L 4 and L 5.

D. *Sprint training*

– 100-m sprints. Number: 5 to 10 x. With 30 to 45 seconds recovery or preferably the same time quietly swimming.
Without diving.
Swimming speed = 1.29 m/sec.
So 100 m in 1 min. 17 sec. to 1 min. 18 sec.
– 50-m sprints. Number: 10 to 15 x. With 30 to 45 seconds recovery.
Swimming speed = 1.43 m/sec., so 50-m time is about 35 sec.
– 25-m sprints. Number: 10 to 20 x. With 30 to 45 seconds recovery.
Swimming speed = 1.57 m/sec., so 25-m time is 15 to 16 seconds.

Table for endurance training

V 4 = 1.21 m/sec.					
Intensive		**Extensive**			
Number*	break	L 2	L 3	L 4	L 5
100 m	10 sec.	1.23	1.21	1.19	1.18
	30 sec.	1.20	1.19	1.17	1.15
200 m	10 sec.	2.47	2.45	2.40	2.38
	30 sec.	2.45	2.42	2.38	2.36
400 m	10 sec.	5.38	5.32	5.24	5.19
	30 sec.	5.36	5.29	5.21	5.15
		average time per 100 m			
20 - 45 min. endurance training		1.27	1.25	1.23	1.21

*Number of repetitions at least 3 to 4 times.

Evaluation

When training according to the above plan, it already produced a distinct improvement the first 6 weeks. The performance top of the last 18 months was broken through remarkably fast. In illustration, the times for 100-m freestyle. Last 18 months 100-m times always about 1 min. 5 sec., but mostly somewhat more.

Last 6 weeks 100-m times: 1.03.8 – 1.03.00 – 1.02.6 – 1.02.2.

The personal best on this distance was broken. Also the other swimming distances showed considerable improvement.

127

PERFORMANCE LEVELS MUTUALLY COMPARED

Lactate measuring has become an essential element in sports medical coaching. After lactate determination, training methods and intensity can accurately be indicated. Training analyses show that many people practice their sports in the wrong way. The practical examples summed up in this book are clear. But lactate determination supplies us with other important information. Performance capacity can now be calculated accurately. Questions like: 'Am I good enough for a certain category?' or 'What time can be achieved with my present condition?' can now be answered.

With a known performance capacity, athletes can be compared mutually. For selection purposes this may turn out to be a valuable instrument in the future.

Performance capacity is tested in a condition test. The quality of the test is decisive whether performance capacity is judged well. One of the vital requirements for a reliable condition test is testing the athlete during his normal sport practice. The swimmer in the water, the marathon runner on the road and the cyclist on his bike or bicycle ergometer. A swimmer, tested on a treadmill or bicycle ergometer gives an unreliable picture of the real swimming-specific performance capacity.
Lactate curves should be determined in a sport-specific manner. Only then we are well informed about sport-specific capacity.

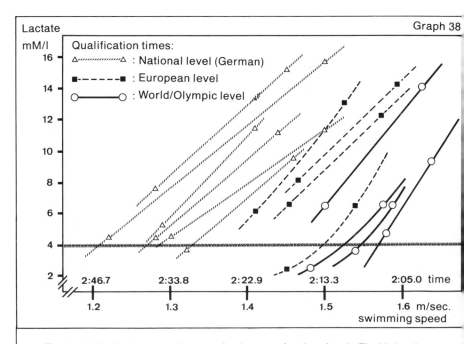

The lactate/swimming speed curves of swimmers of various levels. The higher the level, the higher the V 4 speed. The V 4 speed is decisive for the racing results.

What is to be understood by sport-specific performance capacity?
It is the pace reached at **lactate 4**; the so-called **V 4 pace**.

The pace reached at lactate 4 is an important indication of the real performance capacity. Any improvement of this V 4 pace always goes together with an improvement of performance capacity. On the basis of this V 4 pace, time needed for races can be predicted. Regularly establishing the V 4 pace expresses whether the athlete is in shape.

For runners and swimmers this V 4 is expressed in meters per second. For cyclists V 4 is expressed in watts (W), this being a measure for the capacity supplied.

Swimmers

The table below compares the V 4 speed for swimmers of various levels. At a certain level there is a certain V 4 speed. If one does not come up to that, the performances will turn out bad.

V 4 m/sec.	100 m		200 m		400 m	
Level	females	males	females	males	females	males
National (German)	1.331	1.440	1.281	1.304	1.177	1.343
European	1.467	1.565	1.412	1.478	1.264	1.480
World	1.553	1.634	1.473	1.531	1.438	1.532

Table: the average sport-specific endurance capacity on various distances. The higher the level, the higher V 4.

Cyclists

When cyclists of various categories are compared mutually, a progressive performance capacity at 2 mM and 4 mM (the aerobic and anaerobic threshold)

129

is seen. From novice, junior, amateur to professional the lactate curve gradually moves to the right.

	Novice 15-16 yr	Junior 17-18 yr	Amateur	Professional
Watts at 2 mM	200	270	320	360
Watts at 4 mM	270	315	376	425

When cyclists of the same category are compared mutually, we find clear differences between the one and the other.

4 professionals	P 1	P 2	P 3	P 4
Watts at 2 mM	360	345	320	320
Watts at 4 mM	425	394	380	371

One is right in supposing that professional cyclists, tested in the same period, show a similar state of conditioning.

The differences in their lactate values must be explained by mutually differentiated talents.
P 1 is very successful professional cyclist, 26 years old.
P 2 and P 3 are neoprofessionals. P 2 has had some remarkable successes, as was expected.
P 4 is a classic example of the helper, the domestique, in his professional career he has perfectly made the best of his limited talents.
P 3, the less talented neoprofessional, has estimated his possibilities less well and at the beginning of this year he was dismissed from a big cycling team which took him on the year before.
We may state for sure that performance capacity of cyclists is very well reflected in their lactate curves.

Long-distance runners

Comparison of running times with laboratory tests at 4 mM (in km/h)

Table 1 shows the athletes, ordered according to their performance in the laboratory at 4 mM (km/h and PR on a treadmill).

Tables II, III and IV show the comparison between the best times of the long-distance runners in races and the laboratory results at 4 mM.
It is remarkable that the same order is practically always obtained and that the race results correlate perfectly with the test results at 4 mM.

Table I Long-distance runners

Order	Name	Performance at 4 mM	
		km/h	PR
1	G.W.	21.2	179
2	M.D.	21.2	185
3	V.M.	21.0	176
4	D.E.	20.7	175
5	B.H.	19.8	177
6	D.S.E.	19.8	189
7	D.G.	19.7	176
8	M.G.	18.6	168
9	L.J.M.	18.0	176
10	V.L.	17.8	170
11	P.R.	17.75	185
12	E.A.	17.6	164
13	G.L.	15.8	178

Table II Aerobic endurance of short duration (2 - 8 minutes)

Name	Time	Order results 4 mM test
1500 m		
1. G.W.	3.40.02	1
2. V.M.	3.45.16	3
3000 m		
1. G.W.	7.55	1
2. D.S.E.	8.22	6
3. B.H.	8.24	5
4. D.E.	8.30	4
5. D.G.	8.32	7
6. V.L.	9.10	10
7. E.A.	9.40	12

Table III Aerobic endurance of intermediate duration (up to 15 minutes)

5000 m		
1. G.W.	13.55.28	1
2. M.D.	14.14.03	2
3. V.M.	14.23	3
4. D.E.	14.30	4
5. D.S.E.	14.39	6
6. B.H.	14.43	5
7. D.G.	14.52	7
8. V.L.	15.42	10
9. E.A.	17.02	12

Table IV Aerobic endurance of long duration (longer than 15 minutes)

10.000 m		
1. G.W.	29.40	1
2. M.D.	29.43	2
3. D.E.	30.13	4
4. B.H.	30.38	5
5. D.S.E.	30.55	6
6. D.G.	31.37	7
7. V.L.	32.40	10
8. E.A.	35.02	12
Race of 21 km 750 m		
1. M.D.	1h 9.24	2
2. M.G.	1h 9.32	7
3. L.J.M.	1h 9.40	9
4. G.L.	1h 13.02	13
5. P.R.	1h 13.30	11

Comparison of lactate results at various points of time for 4 long-distance runners

Runner 1 was submitted to a lactate test on 17 January and 25 July 1986

	17.01.1986	25.07.1986
Aerobic threshold 2 mM	18.6 km/h	17.1 km/h
Anaerobic threshold 4 mM	21.2 km/h	19.3 km/h

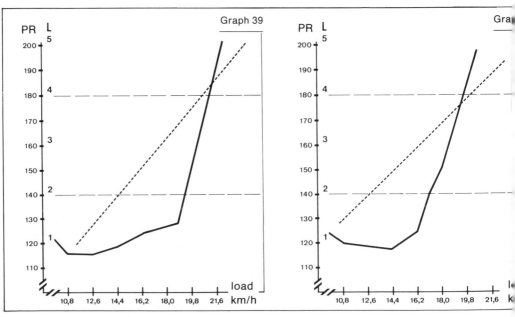

* For reading the PR at L 2 and L 4, see example in graph 42.
The dotted line indicates the relation between PR and lactate. The
uninterrupted line gives the relation between lactate and pace.

The lactate curve has the same shape but the performances on the aerobic and anaerobic threshold have gone down in 6 months after the first test. This deterioration can be explained by an injury, which temporarily forced the athlete to decrease the quantity and intensity of his training.

Long-distance runner 2 was tested on 5 September 1985 and 6 May 1986

	05.09.1985	06.05.1986
Aerobic threshold 2 mM Anaerobic threshold 4 mM	18.0 km/h 19.8 km/h	17.8 km/h 19.7 km/h

The performances at 2 and 4 mM are practically identical. The lactate curves run practically equal from 2 mM onward. Under these 2 mM the curve of 06.05.1986 runs lower.

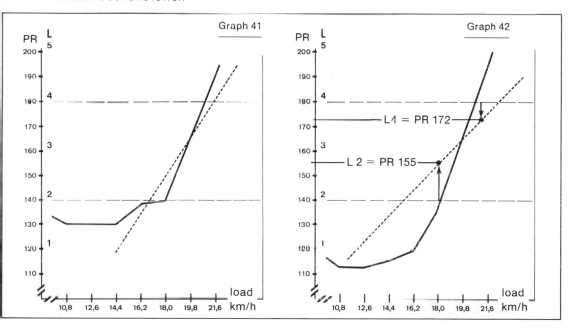

Long-distance runner 3 was submitted to a lactate test on 26 November 1985 and on 15 April 1986

	26.11.1985	15.04.1986
Aerobic threshold 2 mM Anaerobic threshold 4 mM	17.3 km/h 20.0 km/h	18.5 km/h 21.2 km/h

This athlete scored a distinct improvement in all the aspects of his endurance capacity. This resulted in a remarkable progress as a long-distance runner and in very good racing results. He even became Belgian National Champion 1986 in a long-distance run for seniors.

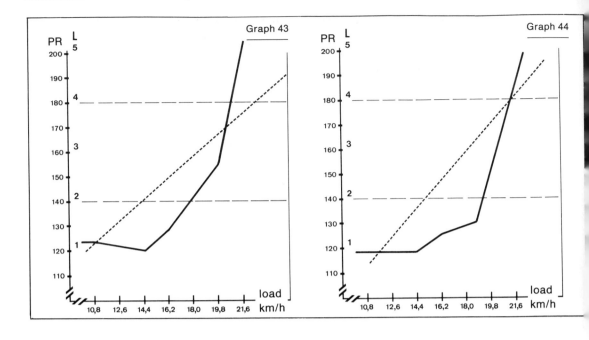

Long-distance runner 4 did a lactate test on 3 September 1985 and on 25 July 1986

	03.09.1985	25.07.1986
Aerobic threshold 2 mM	16.2 km/h	17.2 km/h
Anaerobic threshold 4 mM	18.5 km/h	19.2 km/h

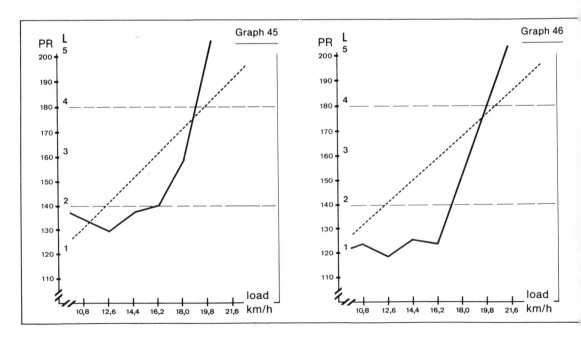

134

This runner has also a remarkable improvement of his test results. It is striking that he has the same pulse rates at 2 mM and 4 mM on the two dates. However, in practice he runs almost 1 km/h faster.
From this comparison of distance runners at various points in time the possibility clearly appears to evaluate the condition of athletes in a correct way.

In conclusion of this chapter, another scheme (after Mader) of
running pace at the 4 mM limit in long-distance runners.

Untrained	between 3 and 3.5 m/sec.	between 10.8 and 12.6 km/h
Slightly trained	3.5 and 4	12.6 and 14.4
Intermediate	4 and 4.7	14.4 and 16.92
Very well	4.8 and 5.2	17.28 and 18.72
Top	5.3 and 5.6	19.08 and 20.16

After their consent a large part of this chapter was taken from a publication by Geert and Piet Leinders, sports physicians at Merelbeke, Belgium.

Motorcar racers

Remarkably high pulse rates are seen in car races. In spite of the relatively slight movement of their own bodies, external factors such as high temperatures, concentration, mental stress, deceleration and acceleration forces and pressure cause such high pulse rates that from start to finish the anaerobic threshold is reached or surpassed. According to Huub Rothengatter's findings his pulse rate at the start is 180. In the course of the race PR remains at this level.

A NUMBER OF PR REGISTRATIONS FROM PRACTICE

Team time trial of a 23-year-old pro cyclist

Test data:
Lactate 2 = PR 165   Maximum PR = 197
Lactate 3 = PR 175
Lactate 4 = PR 180

The registration is one of a team time trial in Paris during the Tour de France 1986.

The first part is the warm-up. During the race, until 55 minutes, he performs well over the level of L 4 = PR 180.

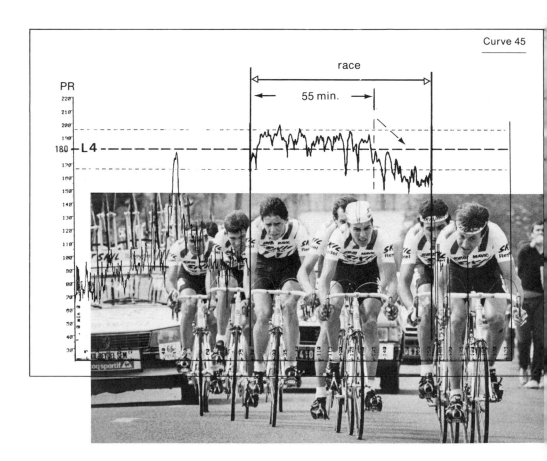

Curve 45

The maximum PR reached in the race is 197. After 55 minutes he cannot keep up with his teammates any more. At this point he has reached maximum acidosis and therefore cannot follow the pace of the team. Yet he keeps performing up to his limits in order to finish in time. If he should not succeed in this, he is out of the race. In spite of the fact that, subjectively, he exerts himself maximally, his PR goes down and so does his cycling speed. So he has been overexerting himself above the deflection point. The curve clearly shows that well-trained athletes can perform high in the anaerobic range for a long period of time.

Aerobic training workout by a pro cyclist

Test data:

Lactate 2 = PR 150   Maximum PR = 175
Lactate 3 = PR 155
Lactate 4 = PR 160

The curve is a reflection of a training workout of endurance capacity.

This workout was carried out in two different manners:
1. In blocks, with short recovery pauses.
2. Continual, so without recovery pauses.

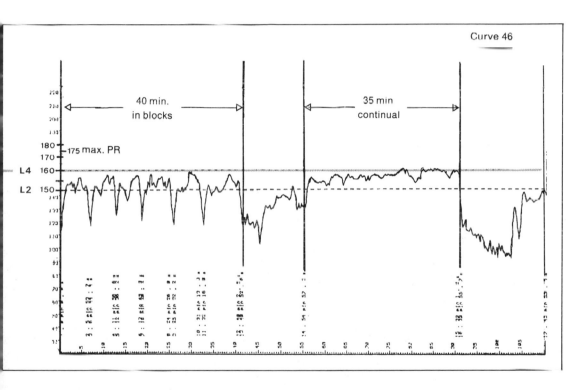

Curve 46

Conclusion:

Correct training of the aerobic system. During the exercise parts, both the blocks and the continual part, PR is between 150 and 160, so also between L 2 and L 4.

Training and time trial registration of a 22-year-old pro cyclist

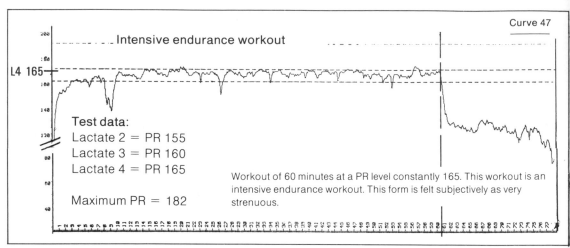

Curve 47

Intensive endurance workout

Test data:
Lactate 2 = PR 155
Lactate 3 = PR 160
Lactate 4 = PR 165

Maximum PR = 182

Workout of 60 minutes at a PR level constantly 165. This workout is an intensive endurance workout. This form is felt subjectively as very strenuous.

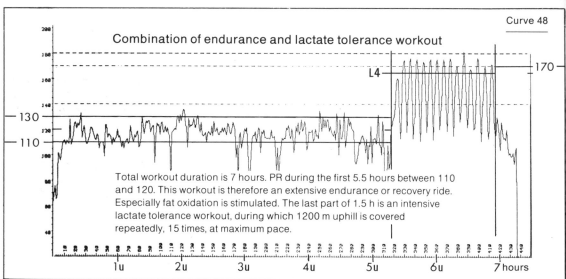

Curve 48

Combination of endurance and lactate tolerance workout

Total workout duration is 7 hours. PR during the first 5.5 hours between 110 and 120. This workout is therefore an extensive endurance or recovery ride. Especially fat oxidation is stimulated. The last part of 1.5 h is an intensive lactate tolerance workout, during which 1200 m uphill is covered repeatedly, 15 times, at maximum pace.

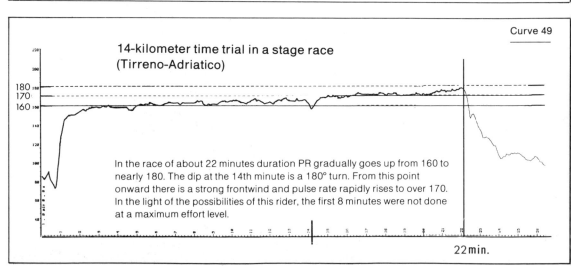

Curve 49

14-kilometer time trial in a stage race
(Tirreno-Adriatico)

In the race of about 22 minutes duration PR gradually goes up from 160 to nearly 180. The dip at the 14th minute is a 180° turn. From this point onward there is a strong frontwind and pulse rate rapidly rises to over 170. In the light of the possibilities of this rider, the first 8 minutes were not done at a maximum effort level.

22 min.

Extensive endurance workout of a triathlete

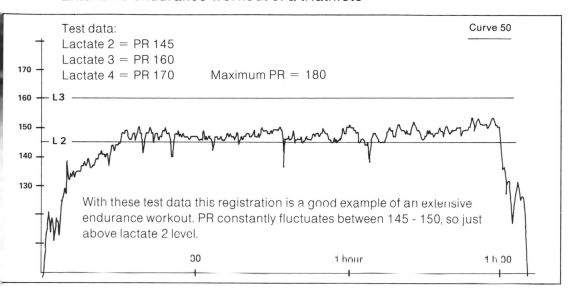

Test data:
Lactate 2 = PR 145
Lactate 3 = PR 160
Lactate 4 = PR 170   Maximum PR = 180

Curve 50

With these test data this registration is a good example of an extensive endurance workout. PR constantly fluctuates between 145 - 150, so just above lactate 2 level.

Conclusion: correct extensive endurance workout.

Triathlete Gregor Stam.

Sprint workouts of a pro cyclist

Test data:
Lactate 2 = PR 150
Lactate 3 = PR 155
Lactate 4 = PR 160   Maximum PR = 175

Task: A warm-up followed by a sprint workout.
Exertion phases are 10 to 20 seconds.
Recovery pauses are long, 3 to 5 minutes.
PR gradually goes up to maximum PR.

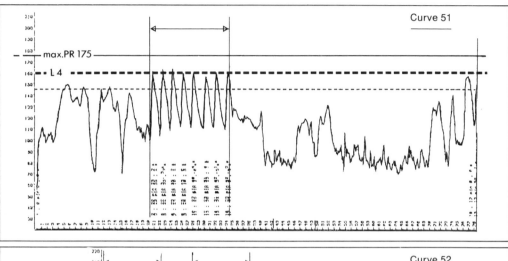

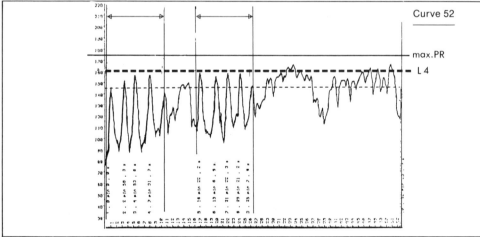

Conclusion:
PR does not surpass 160. Possibly the rider had insufficiently recovered from the previous workout. The recovery pauses are too short. During sprint workouts high lactate contents should not be reached, so recovery pauses must be long. Sprint workouts are only then fruitful when complete recuperation has taken place.

During sprint workouts PR goes up somewhat higher with every rush. Eventually maximum PR is reached. In these curves maximum PR is not reached.

Aerobic training workout by a pro cyclist

Test data:
Lactate 2 = PR 150
Lactate 3 = PR 155
Lactate 4 = PR 160   Maximum PR = 175

The task was doing an aerobic workout in blocks and continual pace.

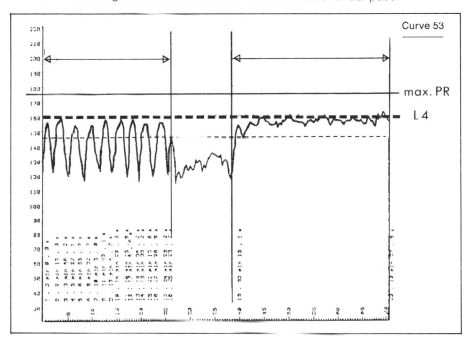

The curve shows:
1. Short exertion blocks, with a duration of 1 - 2 minutes. PR rises to 160.
   Recovery pauses are short, PR goes down to 120.
2. Continual pace, without recovery breaks, during 30 minutes PR is between
   150 and 160.

The first part of the workout is in fact anaerobic. The aerobic system is more or
less slow. It takes some minutes before the aerobic system has come in full
operation.
In itself this workout is not bad at all, but the task has not been done. When
executed like this, it as an anaerobic interval workout, during which PR drops to
120 in the recovery pauses.

Observation:
During a training method in blocks the exertion phases must be longer: longer
than 3 minutes, e.g., 3 - 5 - 8 minutes. The continual method must take 20 to 60
minutes. The intensity of the continual workout is right. During the exertion
phase PR is between 150 and 160, so between L 2 and L 4.

141

Power training workout by a pro cyclist

Test data:
Lactate 2 = PR 150
Lactate 3 = PR 155
Lactate 4 = PR 160   Maximum PR = 175

The curve reflects a power training workout on the bicycle.
Task: sitting on the saddle ride uphill or in frontwind with a big gear.

Duration of the exertion phases between 1 and 5 minutes. Number of repetitions:
4 to 10 x at the most. PR goes up in peaks over 160.

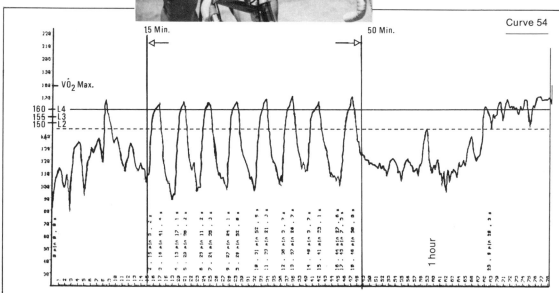

Curve 54

Commentary
Training workout well executed. Recovery is good. PR quickly drops to 90.

PULSE RATE REGISTRATIONS FROM DIFFERENT FIELDS

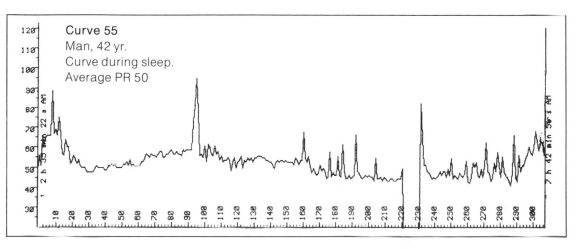

Curve 55
Man, 42 yr.
Curve during sleep.
Average PR 50

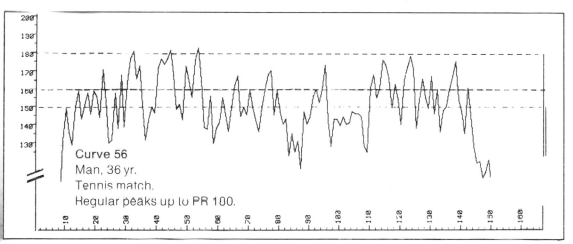

Curve 56
Man, 36 yr.
Tennis match.
Regular peaks up to PR 100.

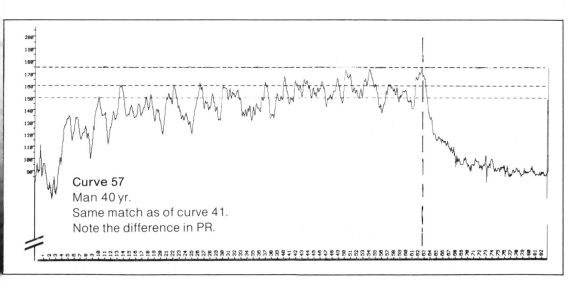

Curve 57
Man 40 yr.
Same match as of curve 41.
Note the difference in PR.

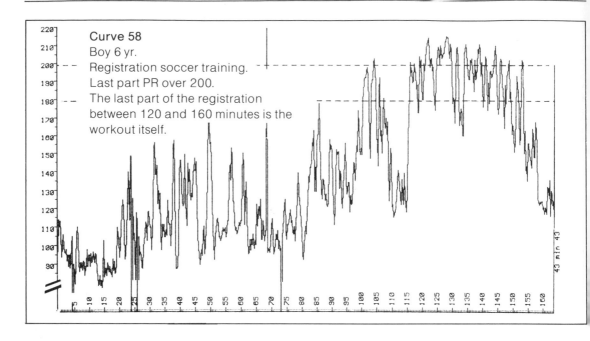

Curve 58
Boy 6 yr.
Registration soccer training.
Last part PR over 200.
The last part of the registration
between 120 and 160 minutes is the
workout itself.

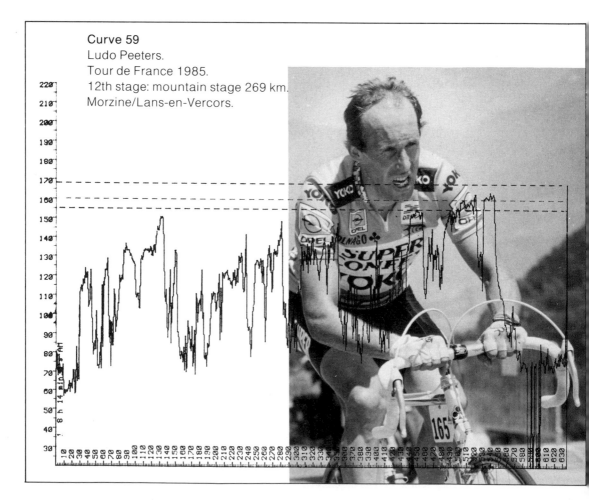

Curve 59
Ludo Peeters.
Tour de France 1985.
12th stage: mountain stage 269 km.
Morzine/Lans-en-Vercors.

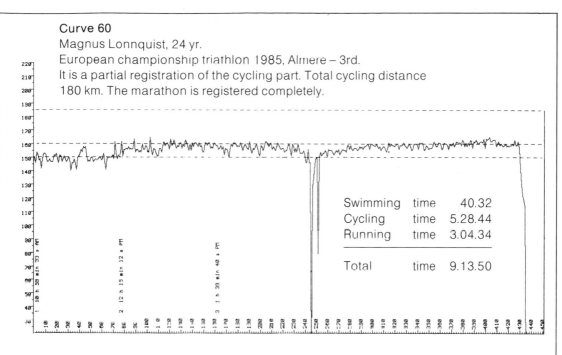

Curve 60

Magnus Lonnquist, 24 yr.

European championship triathlon 1985, Almere – 3rd.

It is a partial registration of the cycling part. Total cycling distance 180 km. The marathon is registered completely.

Swimming	time	40.32
Cycling	time	5.28.44
Running	time	3.04.34
Total	time	9.13.50

PR always fluctuates between 150 and 160. So his deflection point is in this range. PR needs a lot of time (near the 70th minute) to reach this level. An explanation is that the athlete has cooled his body while swimming and this cooling is likely to be the cause of the lower PR at the beginning of the registration. The downward peak is the transition from cycling to running. During attendance the electrode got loose for a moment.

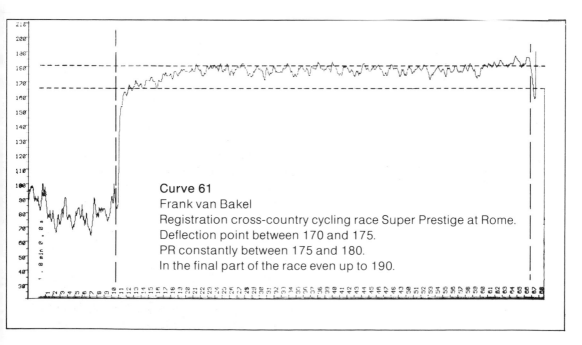

Curve 61

Frank van Bakel

Registration cross-country cycling race Super Prestige at Rome.

Deflection point between 170 and 175.

PR constantly between 175 and 180.

In the final part of the race even up to 190.

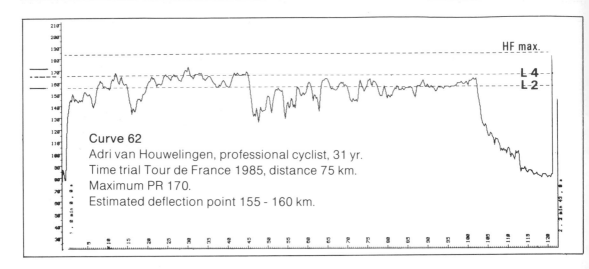

Curve 62
Adri van Houwelingen, professional cyclist, 31 yr.
Time trial Tour de France 1985, distance 75 km.
Maximum PR 170.
Estimated deflection point 155 - 160 km.

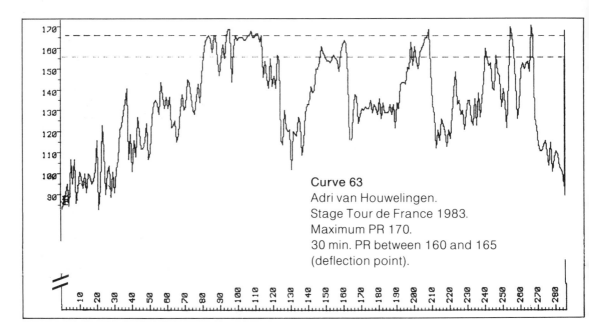

Curve 63
Adri van Houwelingen.
Stage Tour de France 1983.
Maximum PR 170.
30 min. PR between 160 and 165
(deflection point).

Explanatory notes for curves 61 - 62 - 63 Adri van Houwelingen
In the Tour de France maximum PR is not reached. Also the PR level at which
performance can be maintained a long time is considerably lower than in the
time trial at Dronten. An explanation is that during the Tour de France the
cyclists always approach a state of overtraining.
When overtrained, there is a decrease of maximum pulse rate; the deflection
point goes down as well. The cyclist was well rested when he began the time trial
at Dronten. Maximum PR then quickly recovers to the old level and also the
deflection point goes to a higher PR.

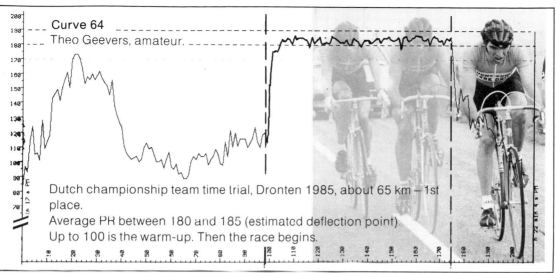

Curve 64

Theo Geevers, amateur.

Dutch championship team time trial, Dronten 1985, about 65 km – 1st place.

Average PR between 180 and 185 (estimated deflection point).

Up to 100 is the warm-up. Then the race begins.

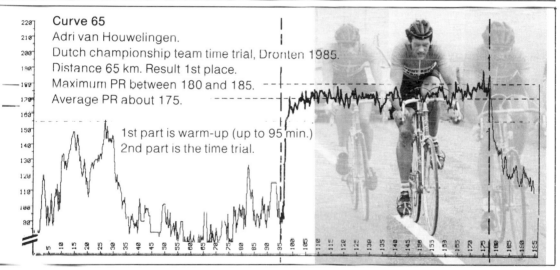

Curve 65

Adri van Houwelingen.

Dutch championship team time trial, Dronten 1985.

Distance 65 km. Result 1st place.

Maximum PR between 180 and 185.

Average PR about 175.

1st part is warm-up (up to 95 min.)

2nd part is the time trial.

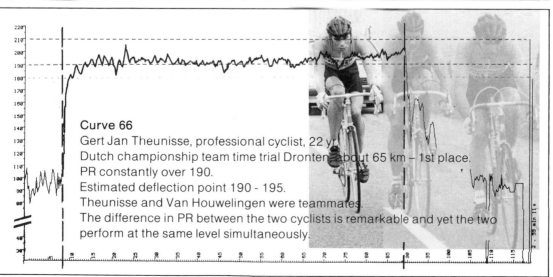

Curve 66

Gert Jan Theunisse, professional cyclist, 22 yr.

Dutch championship team time trial Dronten, about 65 km – 1st place.

PR constantly over 190.

Estimated deflection point 190 - 195.

Theunisse and Van Houwelingen were teammates.

The difference in PR between the two cyclists is remarkable and yet the two perform at the same level simultaneously.

147

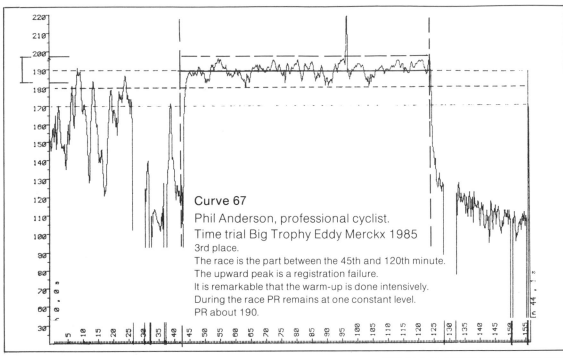

Curve 67

Phil Anderson, professional cyclist.

Time trial Big Trophy Eddy Merckx 1985

3rd place.

The race is the part between the 45th and 120th minute.

The upward peak is a registration failure.

It is remarkable that the warm-up is done intensively.

During the race PR remains at one constant level.

PR about 190.

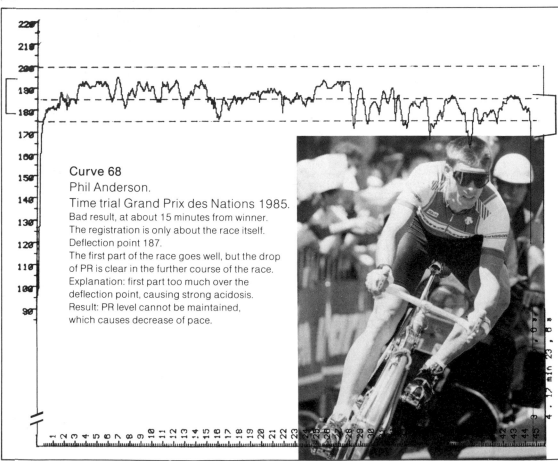

Curve 68

Phil Anderson.

Time trial Grand Prix des Nations 1985.

Bad result, at about 15 minutes from winner.

The registration is only about the race itself.

Deflection point 187.

The first part of the race goes well, but the drop

of PR is clear in the further course of the race.

Explanation: first part too much over the

deflection point, causing strong acidosis.

Result: PR level cannot be maintained,

which causes decrease of pace.

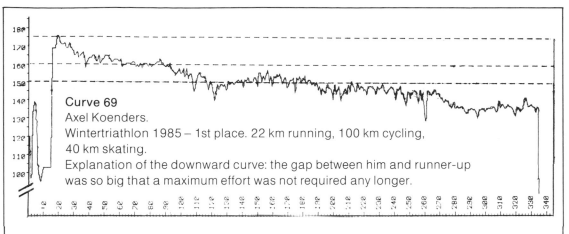

Curve 69
Axel Koenders.
Wintertriathlon 1985 – 1st place. 22 km running, 100 km cycling,
40 km skating.
Explanation of the downward curve: the gap between him and runner-up
was so big that a maximum effort was not required any longer.

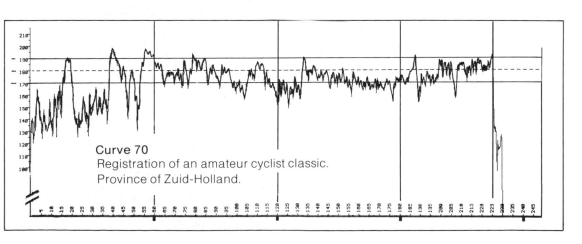

Curve 70
Registration of an amateur cyclist classic.
Province of Zuid-Holland.

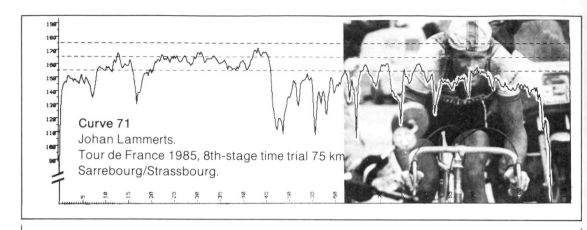

Curve 71
Johan Lammerts.
Tour de France 1985, 8th-stage time trial 75 km
Sarrebourg/Strassbourg.

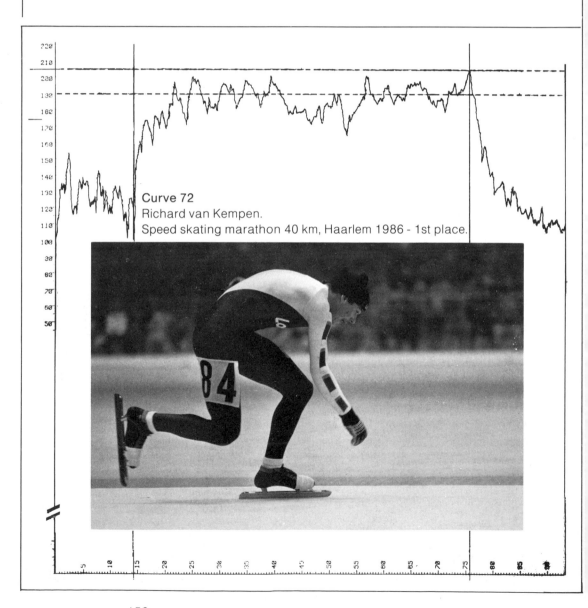

Curve 72
Richard van Kempen.
Speed skating marathon 40 km, Haarlem 1986 - 1st place.

World hour record Hilbert van der Duim

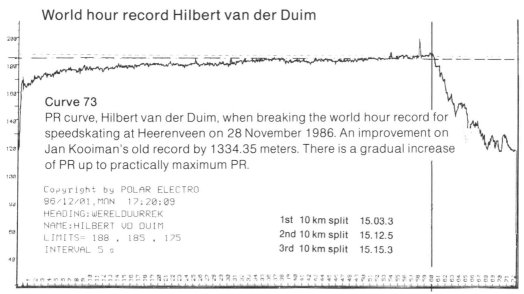

Curve 73
PR curve, Hilbert van der Duim, when breaking the world hour record for speedskating at Heerenveen on 28 November 1986. An improvement on Jan Kooiman's old record by 1334.35 meters. There is a gradual increase of PR up to practically maximum PR.

Copyright by POLAR ELECTRO
86/12/01,MON 17:20:09
HEADING:WERELDUURREK
NAME:HILBERT VD DUIM
LIMITS= 188 , 185 , 175
INTERVAL 5 s

1st 10 km split	15.03.3
2nd 10 km split	15.12.5
3rd 10 km split	15.15.3

Explanation of the curve for Hilbert van der Duim

The gradual increase of PR may be explained as follows:
The record attempt took place in the roof-topped Thialf ice-hall. The number of spectators was 10,000. An account of this temperature in the hall during this record attempt went up to 20 °C (68 °F). Cooling the body was strongly minimized and perspiration increased considerably. Fluid loss must have been substantial. The athlete did not drink during his attempt. The combination of these factors caused body temperature to go up gradually, which always goes together with a rise in pulse rate.
C.f. chapters 'Influence of cooling during exertion on pulse rate' and 'Fluid loss and pulse rate'.

* On 29 November 1988 Robert Vunderink (the Netherlands) improved this world hour record from 39.492 km to 39.986 km.

ANALYSES OF A NUMBER OF TRAINING WORKOUTS

Cross-country cycling

	Participants												
	1	2	3	4	5	6	7	8	9	10	11	12	13
Lt 1	8.2	5.0	4.3	4.2	15.7	11.1	8.9	4.1	3.9	7.2	7.2	12.5	8.5
Lt 2	8.7				14.3	9.8	10.7			4.8	4.8	12.1	12.6

Lactate values Lt 1 and Lt 2 were determined at 2 different moments during a group workout of 13 cross-country cyclists.

There was no training task set. It was an average workout, which is done 2 to 3 times a week at this intensity. Participants 12 and 13 were registered by telemetry (see graphs 47 and 48).

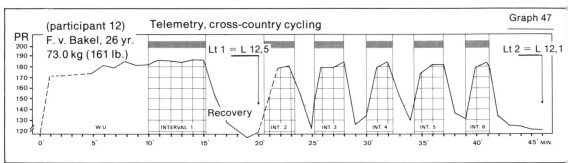

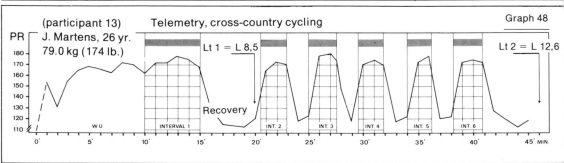

Commentary: The various participants reach strongly different lactate values. That means that this workout has on one athlete a totally different effect as on the other. Participants 2, 3, 4, 8 and 9 are training their aerobic capacity. The other participants reach high lactate values. That means that lactate tolerance is trained. Three workouts of this kind per week together with the races during weekends form too heavy a workload.

A maximum performance level cannot be maintained with this quantity of training load. The high lactate burdens cause damage to the aerobic endurance capacity. It is due to this training zeal that man cross-country cyclists have a strong decline in the course of the season. It is a lot of trouble indeed to convince athletes to change their training routine and limit the number of workouts during which high lactate values are reached.

They should be replaced by workouts training the aerobic endurance capacity, during which lactate content does not surpass 6.

Many athletes are not satisfied unless they feel as though they have been 'torn to pieces' after a training workout. The same feeling of fatigue as in the races must be reached, they think. This feeling is caused by high lactate contents. By just changing the mix of the training workouts, their level of performance can be maintained and for many of them even improved considerably.

Swimming workouts

Determination of lactate values during a sprint workout by 5 swimmers.

Task: about 16 seconds of maximum effort, followed by some 16 seconds of recovery. The total training time is 30 minutes. During sprint training the creatine phosphate system is stressed. High lactate values are undesirable in a sprint workout. The arising of high lactic acid values is an expression of the use of the lactate system.
Lactate values in a sprint workout must not surpass 6 to 7 mM.

	Participants				
	1	2	3	4	5
L 10 min.	5.9	14.0			
L 20 min.	7.0	14.0			
L 30 min.	6.4	14.6	5.8	4.3	5.6

Commentary: again we find clearly different lactate values during exactly the same training task. Participant 2 immediately strikes the eye. By taking longer recovery breaks or by lowering the intensity of the sprints, lactate content will go up less high. Only then his workout will become a real sprint workout.
Participants 1, 2, 4 and 5 reach good lactate values, meaning that for them this sprint workout went well.

Sprint workout with 13 participants.
Task: 30 seconds of maximum swimming, then 15 seconds recovery.

	Participants												
	1	2	3	4	5	6	7	8	9	10	11	12	13
L	7.0	7.2	4.1	12.0	6.3	6.6	7.8	5.1	4.0	5.5	11.9	10.1	6.7

Training sprints is training the creatine phosphate system. Lactate values over 6 to 7 must not be reached.

Commentary: The lactate values during this group workout show big

153

differences. All participants had the same task.

A large percentage of the participants do not do a sprint workout, but a lactate tolerance workout. The training task is not well understood. They lack the right feeling of the intensity of training.

Swimming workout with 5 participants.

Protocol: after a 15-minute warm-up there is a 30-minute endurance workout. The intensity of this endurance workout is as the participants are normally accustomed to. After 15 and after 30 minutes of endurance work, lactate content is determined (Lt 1 and Lt 2).

Then there is a recovery period of 20 minutes, followed by an interval workout with the task: 12 x 60 m at 80% of maximum intensity. Halfway and at the end of the interval workout lactate content is determined again (Lt 3 and Lt 4).

	Participants				
	1	2	3	4	5
Lt 1	3.3	1.7	1.6	4.9	2.7
Lt 2	2.4	1.8	1.6	4.3	1.4
Lt 3	1.0	1.3	4.9	8.4	1.8
Lt 4	1.2	1.0	2.9	8.8	1.4

Commentary: only participant 4 carries out the training task according to plan. The intensity of his endurance training is right. The training impulse is excellent for an ideal use of the aerobic energy-supplying system. Number 4's intervals are also right.

The lactate values that are reached are sufficiently high, which means that the lactate system is sufficiently taxed.

For the other participants 1, 2, 3 and 5 the workout failed more or less. The tasks set are not carried out by the swimmers as they should have been, for an ideal endurance workout takes place in the lactic acid range between 2 and 4 mM, tolerance training between 6 and 10 mM lactate.

Cycling training

Bicycling workout with 3 participants on a hilly route (Berg en Dal near Nijmegen, the Netherlands).

Task: Four laps are ridden with maximum intensity. At the end of each lap, ending with an uphill $2\frac{1}{2}$ km, a lactate determination is done.

During this workout pulse rates are continually registered (curves 74, 75 and 76).

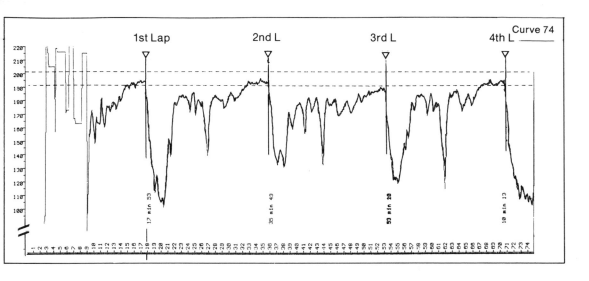

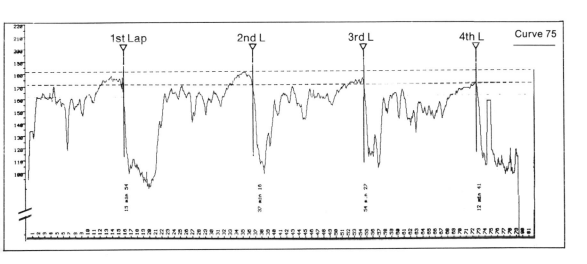

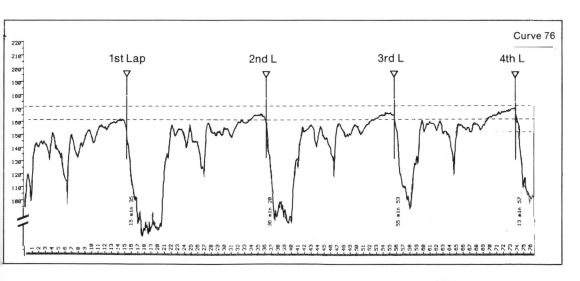

	Participants			
	1	2	3	
Lt 1	9.1	9.1	7.6	1st lap
Lt 2	7.0	8.6	7.3	2nd lap
Lt 3	3.7	5.1	8.2	3rd lap
Lt 4	5.6	4.8	12.0	4th lap

Commentary: For every participant there is the same conclusion. This workout is an ideal training of tolerance capacity, i.e., the lactate system. For training endurance (aerobic capacity) this workout is too intensive. This kind of workout once a week is more than enough. When many races are done, such a workout is not necessary at all. Then the races themselves form an ideal training to improve lactate tolerance capacity.

Training long-distance runners

Lactate values were determined and pulse rates registered on 15 long-distance runners.

Task: A warm-up of 20 minutes is followed by an endurance workout of 30 minutes. Then a recovery period of 15 minutes followed by an interval workout. The endurance and interval workouts are done at an intensity the runners are used to. After 15 minutes of endurance, Lt 1 is determined, and Lt 2 after 30 minutes. Halfway, the interval Lt 3 and at the end Lt 4 are determined.

	Participants														
	1	2	3	4	5	6	7	8	9	10	11	12	13	14	15
Lt 1	2.3	1.5	1.1	2.6	0.8	0.8	1.0	1.5	1.1	2.2	1.7	5.1			
Lt 2	1.3	1.4	0.9	1.8	0.8	0.6	0.9	1.4	0.8	2.5	1.9	5.1	4.2	1.4	0.9
Lt 3	0.8	2.9	7.3	6.4	8.3	4.1	10.1	10.0	9.9	8.0	5.8	11.1	5.7	8.6	4.4
Lt 4	0.8	2.9	5.8	7.2	9.7	8.4	8.5	12.3	7.7	10.1	6.8	9.9	6.9	9.4	5.2

Commentary: Training stimulus is right for endurance training when during this workout lactate values are reached between 2 and 4 mM lactate. During this workout the intensity is too low for 12 out of 15 runners. Only runners 10, 12 and 13 do their endurance work at the right intensity. The slight acidification in runner 12 probably has no negative effect. Slightly surpassing the 4 mM limit during endurance workout has little meaning. It would be ideal to determine the deflection point of this runner exactly to be completely sure of the right training intensity. The intervals, as a training workout for the lactate system, require lactate values between 6 and 10 mM lactate.
This workout has gone better for most runners, but here again there are some runners who do not carry out the task as they should.

The pulse rate curves of the 15 runners tested

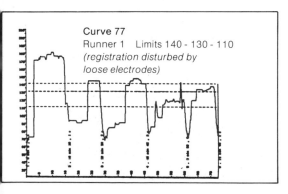

Curve 77
Runner 1   Limits 140 - 130 - 110
(registration disturbed by loose electrodes)

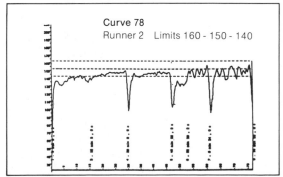

Curve 78
Runner 2   Limits 160 - 150 - 140

Curve 79
Runner 3
Limits 190 - 170 - 150

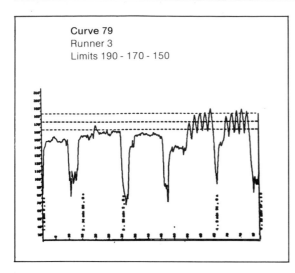

Curve 80
Runner 4
Limits 190 - 170 - 150

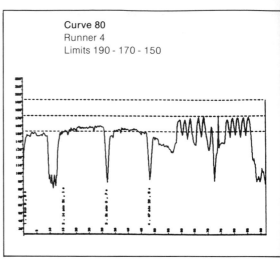

Curve 81
Runner 5
Endurance PR 160
Intervals PR 180

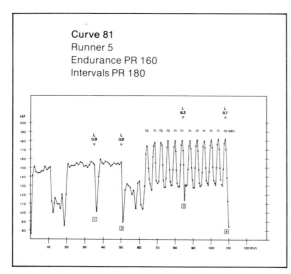

Curve 82
Runner 6
Limits 190 - 170 - 150

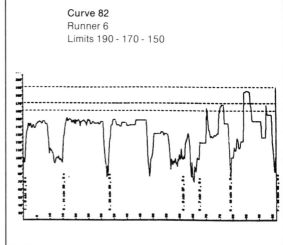

Curve 83
Runner 7
Limits 180 - 160 - 140

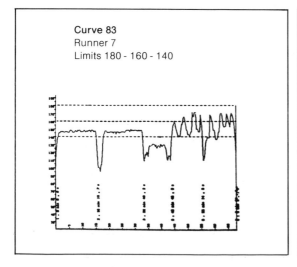

Curve 84
Runner 8
Limits 190 - 170 - 150

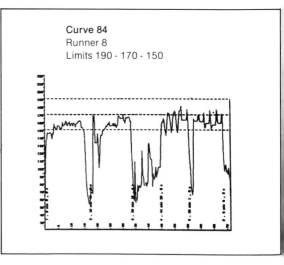

Curve 85
Runner 9
Limits 190 - 170 - 150

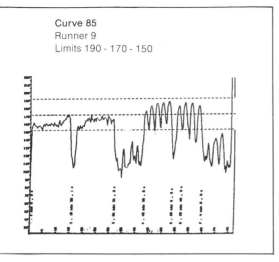

Curve 86
Runner 10
Limits 190 - 170 - 150

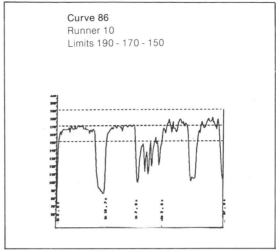

Curve 87
Runner 11
Limits 190 - 170 - 150

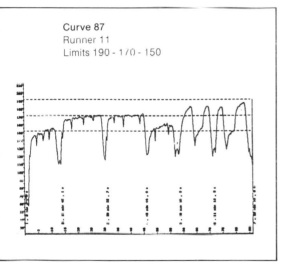

Curve 88
Runner 12
Limits 160 - 150 - 140

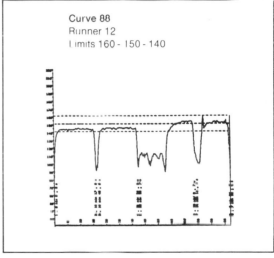

Curve 89
Runner 13
Limits 190 - 170 - 150
(registration disturbed)

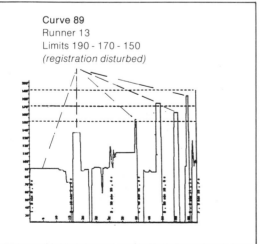

Curve 90
Runner 14
Limits 180 - 160 - 140

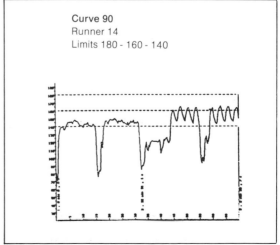

159

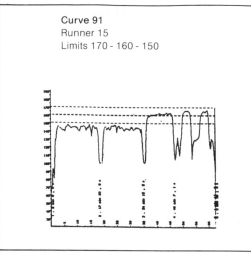

Curve 91
Runner 15
Limits 170 - 160 - 150

Endurance run with distance runners.

For 3 long-distance runners lactate determination and PR registrations were done (curves 92 and 93).

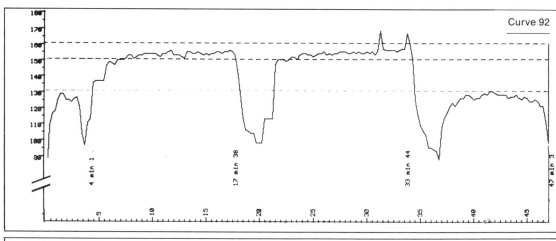

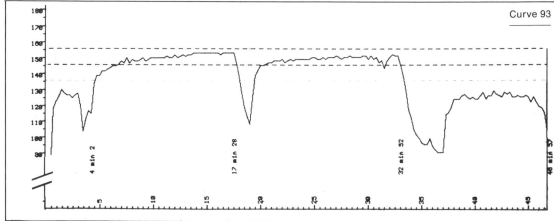

Task: Do an endurance run of 30 minutes at your normal intensity.
Lactate was determined after 15 minutes and once again after half an hour
(thus at the end of the workout).
PR curve of runner 1 is not available.

	Participants		
	1	2	3
L 15 min.	4.0	7.5	9.5
L 30 min.	4.1	9.1	10.9

Commentary:
Athlete 1: good endurance workout at
the right intensity.
Athletes 2 and 3: these athletes did
not do an endurance but a tolerance
workout. The training task was not
carried out as it should have been.

Soccer

Training

Task: Run 6 x uphill at maximum
pace. When PR has gone down to
120, make another start.
During this form of training, maximum
lactate values are reached between
15 and 24 mM. The high lactate
values require a recovery period of at
least 18 hours. In this period the risk
of injury is enormous. Training
technical skills cannot be done well
because coordination is disturbed in
this recovery period.
This kind of training workout often
occurs in soccer. The result is a
decrease of endurance capacity. For
these reasons this kind of workout
during the preparatory phase can
best be abstained from.

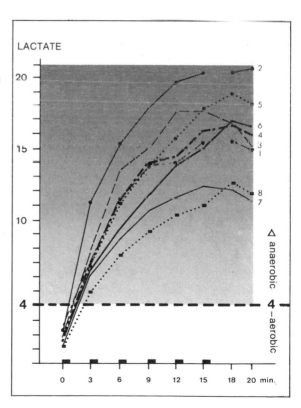

Lactate curves of 8 soccer players during a
workout in the preparatory phase before the
new season.

Source: Deutsche Zeitschrift für Sportmedizin,
Heft 1/1985, Trainingssteuerung im Hochleistungssport:
einige Aspekte und Beispiele,
von Liesen e.a., p. 8-18.

Match

In order to establish whether a soccer player performs intensely in a match, investigations were done into pulse rate and lactate content. It appears to be so that top soccer players have pulse rates over 85% of their maximum during a large part of the match.

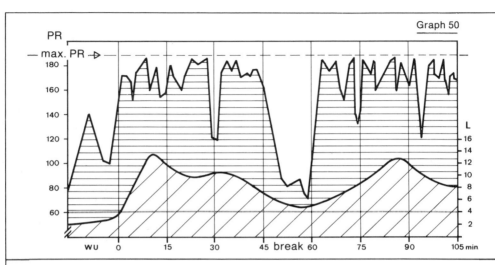

Pulse rate and blood lactate of a center player during a soccer match in the Swedish first division.

For professional soccer players in Sweden the average oxygen intake in a normal match turns out to be almost 80% of the $\dot{V}O_2$ max. This means that a soccer player should have an excellent aerobic endurance capacity and a soccer-specific anaerobic endurance capacity. From the above figure it appears that a soccer player while playing a match may reach lactate values between 4 and 14.

The exertion in a soccer match often has an anaerobic character with all the nasty consequences of it, such as disturbed coordination and an enhanced risk of injury.

Source: Ekblom B., 'Applied Physiology of Soccer', in: American Journal of Sports Medicine (1986), nr. 3, p. 50-60.

Training workout of a 17-year-old sprinter

Three series are run: 5 x 50 m, 5 x 60 m and 5 x 70 m.

Lactate after warm-up: 4.3.
Lactate after 3 minutes cool-down run: 2.9 (starting lactate).

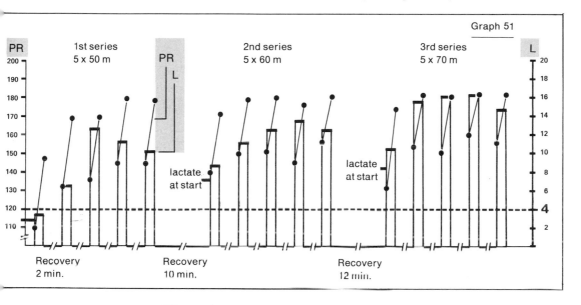

Graph 51

First series:				Lactate at start 2.9	
meters	PR	PR	time	recovery	lactate
1st 50	110 > 147		5.8 sec.	2 min.	3.7
2nd 50	132 > 168		5.9 sec.	2 min.	6.3
3rd 50	136 > 169		5.9 sec.	2 min.	12.8
4th 50	145 > 179		6.0 sec.	2 min.	11.2
5th 50	145 > 178		6.0 sec.	2 min.	10.2

After this series a cool-down run of 10 minutes.

Second series:				Lactate at start 7.1	
meters	PR	PR	time	recovery	lactate
1st 60	140 >	172	6.8 sec.	2 min.	8.6
2nd 60	150 >	179	7.0 sec.	2 min.	11.1
3rd 60	151 >	180	7.3 sec.	2 min.	12.6
4th 60	145 >	176	6.9 sec.	2 min.	13.5
5th 60	157 >	180	6.9 sec.	2 min.	12.7

After this series a cool-down run of 12 minutes.

Third series:				Lactate at start 8.3	
meters	PR	PR	time	recovery	lactate
1st 70	132 >	174	8.2 sec.	2 min.	10.6
2nd 70	154 >	181	8.0 sec.	2 min.	15.5
3rd 70	151 >	180	8.3 sec.	2 min.	16.1
4th 70	161 >	181	8.4 sec.	2 min.	16.2
5th 70	156 >	181	8.4 sec.	2 min.	14.8

Commentary:

This young sprinter trains three to four times a week in this way. The last year there has been no improvement. The number of injuries has gone up. This workout has very high lactate values; it is to be considered as a very intensive lactate tolerance training method. As a sprint workout it is a complete failure. One such intensive workout per week is likely to be more than enough; three to four must cause problems. This must be the reason for the stagnation of performance level and the increased injury risk.

During sprint workout lactate content must not go up so high. In order to avoid this, recovery time must be longer. During this recovery time, creatine phosphate (CP) and ATP (the phosphate battery) get a chance of reforming.

It is striking how high PR is at the start of the sprints.

Analysis

Training analyses indicate, and the literature also gives many examples, that training is often done with the wrong intensity.

Training tasks are often not understood or felt by the athletes. The methods described here are a good instrument to teach the athletes how to listen to the signals of the body. The feeling of the right training intensity can be acquired. Well-instructed athletes are capable of performing at a certain level up to $\frac{1}{2}$ mM accurately. So once you know the feeling of running or cycling with a lactate content of 4 mM, you are capable of practicing your sport again next time with the same intensity.

The workload intensity may be subjectively divided with the help of a scale running from 1 to 5.

Workload intensity:
- 1 = very light effort
- 2 = light effort
- 3 = intermediate effort
- 4 = heavy effort
- 5 = very heavy effort

The judging of the workload intensity after repeated tests is very consistent in the same person.

Especially the better-trained athletes, once they have learned it, can very well indicate subjectively how heavy the effort has been.

The workload intensity of lactate 4 is felt as intermediate. When condition is improved, the workload intensity of lactate 4 also increases. In spite of this increase, the effort will be felt as intermediate.

Once you have learned to feel subjectively how your workload was, it may be a very valuable instrument to optimalize training.

Pro cyclist, ex-world champion Gerrie Knetemann.

RECOMMENDATIONS FOR SPORT IN GENERAL

Finally, we shall take a look at sport in general. The optimal workload of 2-4 mM lactate/l applies, of course, not only to top-class athletes but also to anyone who takes part in sports. It is here, in fact, that one frequently encounters people wrongly training themselves to the point of complete exhaustion and speechlessness. Such activity does not evoke in the organism the desirable adaptation mechanism that would lead to improved performance.

In a study of 50 'spare time' joggers who were invited at random, without being given any previous information, to take part in a lactate test, levels of 6-12 mM/l were measured, with an average of 8.5 mM/l. Measured using an anaerobic threshold of 4 mM lactate/l they all showed a 100% increase in their lactic acid level. A similar result was found for people who went swimming in their spare time. However, to take full advantage of the body's adaptation potential it is necessary to keep to the stated lactate thresholds. For the jogger this means 'running without puffing'.

Since 'spare time athletes' do not usually have the opportunity to measure their blood lactate, they have to rely on the less accurate method of measuring their heart rate. Rules have therefore been drawn up, which are based on the results of research into lactate behavior in sports medicine.

The workload in endurance sports should be at a level that results in heart rates of 130-160 beats/min. in healthy men and women below 50 years of age.

Above the age of 50 one's training should be in line with the following rule of thumb: it should produce a heart rate of 180 minus the age in years. The exercise should last 30-40 min. if it involves running, swimming or cycling. If the training program involves doing this exercise 3 or 4 times a week, optimal adaptation can be anticipated.

These adaptations are divided into peripheral and central mechanisms. The peripheral mechanisms are:
– increases in the number and volume of mitochondria in the trained muscle cells
– increased activity of enzymes with aerobic/anaerobic action
– increased myoglobin content
– reduction in LDL-cholesterol and triglycerides, accompanied by an increase in HDL-cholesterol
– increases in the number and surface area of capillaries in the trained muscle cells
– improved glucose tolerance.

The central adaptations affect the heart itself:
– lower heart rate, both at rest and during exercise
– extension of the diastolic period
– reduced contractility
– consolidation of electrical stability
– reduced catecholamine release.

From the viewpoint of internal medicine the best sports are those that produce the greatest number of beneficial adaptations with the smallest amount of work for the organs. The following list is the result of sports medicine studies of cardiovascular reactions and metabolic behavior. The sports are listed according to the degree of benefit:

1. Jogging
2. Cycling, cross-country skiing, and hiking
3. Swimming
4. Sports such as tennis, basketball, football and handball
5. Rowing.

Jablonski et al. have shown that a running pace based on the 'one-in-four rhythm' (in which one breathes in once over 4 paces and breathes out for the next 4) is most suitable for 'spare time athletes' to achieve the recommended workload. High lactate values were found with one-in-three rhythms and even more so with one-in-two rhythms. Valuable knowledge has therefore been gained on arterial lactate measurement in competitive sport. Since all areas of sport are governed by the same biological laws, this knowledge has also led to recommendations of the type of sporting activity necessary to maintain health in large sectors of the population.

CONCLUSION

A correct build-up of training takes the various energy-supplying systems into consideration. These systems are the *creatine phosphate system* and the *lactic acid system*, which supply energy in an *anaerobic* manner, on the one hand, and on the other, the *glucose and fat oxidation system*, which supplies energy aerobically. The question which system supplies the energy depends on the duration and intensity of the effort.

Roughly speaking, short bursts of exercise are supplied with anaerobic energy and slightly intensive efforts of long duration are supplied with aerobic energy.

Every system requires its specific training routine. Beside specific training for the various systems ample attention should be paid to sufficient recovery after the effort.

Training build-up should primarily be directed at an improvement of the aerobic endurance capacity. The right intensity of a workout for improvement of the aerobic capacity is in the aerobic-anaerobic transition zone – in the lactic acid range between 2-4 mM. Later, when aerobic capacity has increased, the other systems can be trained specifically. By other systems we mean the creatine phosphate system and the lactic acid system.

The various forms of training should be done in the right quantities and the right mixture to complete the whole training program. Whenever one form of training is overemphasized, this will cause a loss of performance capacity.

Many athletes find difficulty in the correct development of the right training program. Serious mistakes are made in both quantity and quality.

The cause of this problem is the fact that people do not know the intensity of their training. By quantifying training workouts better, according to the principles set forth in this book, it is possible to teach the athlete accurately about the intensities with which he trains a certain single system. A well-instructed athlete knows exactly what feeling it is to train with a certain intensity. This feeling can be acquired to an accuracy of $\frac{1}{2}$ mM. So the athlete precisely knows what it means to train at for example 2, 4, 6 or 10 mM lactic acid.

Athletes often train with an incorrectly developed feeling of the right intensity. Especially the overintense workouts, repeated too often, reaching high lactic values, have a *negative* impact on performance capacity. This kind of training is practiced very often.

The athlete who wants to achieve his maximum is willing to 'go for it' in training. He is only 'satisfied' when the feel of the race is also approached in training. This feeling is caused by high lactic values in his blood. Values between 10 and 20 mM are not exceptional. When training is often carried out in this manner the following situation will arise.

The athlete who exerts himself to the limits of his capability cannot reach the desired level in spite of all his efforts. He will then even increase his training workload in order to achieve what he aims for. A further downfall in the performance curve and overtraining may be the result.

The acidosis, caused by the high lactic values in the muscles, damages the aerobic enzymes system. The aerobic enzymes system may be seen as a factory plant where aerobic energy supply is produced. The acidosis is the cause of a deterioration of aerobic endurance capacity. After heavy exercise with high lactic values the body needs some time to let the damaged aerobic enzymes system recover. Therefore, it is always advisable to take a recovery workout the day after a heavy training program.

Various sports require a large aerobic endurance capacity together with a well-developed coordination capacity. Coordination should also be trained separately. For most sports, training coordination is called training technical skills. Training coordination is seriously disturbed at lactic values over 8 mM. Complicated technical movements cannot be performed then. The higher lactic acid goes up, the more difficult it is to handle complicated techniques. So it is of vital importance to bear this in mind when training coordination.

A football player will not be able to acquire technical skills during an exhausting workout. The high lactic content will interfere with coordination, thus rendering his technical training without any benefit.
Not only will football be an example, but also tennis, (speed-)skating, hockey, wrestling, basketball, table-tennis, cross-country cycling and many other sports can be added to this list.

We have seen that a high lactic content arises after and during intensive training. This causes a decrease of aerobic endurance capacity, and coordination may be disturbed.
Furthermore, the risk of injury will be larger. Acidosis in the muscles causes microscopic damage in muscle tissue. This minor damage, when insufficiently recovered, is an ideal basis for major injuries.

Group workouts in various sports are too often not more than well-meant amateurish play. Training tasks set for the complete group have a totally different effect on the group members individually. The one will intensely train his lactic system, the other is doing an aerobic workout. During the same task a third person might even do a recovery workout. *Especially coaches should be aware of the fact that group workouts show these differences.*
At any rate, the conclusion is justified that group workouts do not form an ideal preparation for reaching a maximum performance level.
It is the coach whose task it is to adjust training per individual in such manner that every participant has maximum benefits of his exertion.

A final word
Pulse rate registration, with or without lactate measuring, is an excellent way of getting to know training intensity. Also for non-top athletes this way of coaching is possible and financially attainable.

REFERENCES

Author	Title, etc.
Astrand, P.O.:	Textbook of work physiology. McGraw-Hill Book Company, New York.
Binkhorst:	Anaërobe drempel. Gen. en Sport 3, 1981, p. 78-79.
Van den Bosch, J.:	De test van Conconi in de praktijk.
Claes:	Een evaluatie van BE bepalingen. Sportmedische tijdingen, 1984, p. 2045-2061.
Leo Clijssen/ Rob Delnoy:	De anaërobe drempel in de trainingspraktijk. Doctoraalscriptie inspanningsfysiologie. Vrije Universiteit Amsterdam, juni 1985.
Conconi:	Determination of the anaerobic threshold by a non-invasive field test in runners. J. Appl. Physiol. vol. 52, no. 4, 1982, p. 869-873.
Heck:	Justification of the 4-mmol/Lactate threshold. Int. J. Sports. Med. 6, 1985, p. 117-130.
Hollmann:	Historical remarks on the Development of the Aerobic-Anaerobic Threshold up to 1966. Int. J. Sports. Med. 6, 1985, p. 109-116.
Hollmann, W.:	Sportmedizin – Arbeits- und Trainingsgrundlagen. F.K. Schattauer Verlag, Stuttgart/New York 1980.
Hollmann, W. e.a.:	Die aerobe Leistungsfähigkeit – Aspekte von Gesundheit und Sport. Spektrum der Wissenschaft, 1986, 48-58.
Israel/Weber:	Probleme der langzeit Ausdauer im Sport, Johann Ambrosius Barth, Leipzig 1972.
Jablonski, D. e.a.:	Intensitätssteuerung und Leistungsbeurteilung beim Jogging. Fortschr. Med. 103 (1985) (4), 47-50.
Liessen:	Trainungssteuerung im Hochleistungssport: einige Aspekte und Beispiele. Deutsche Zeitschrift für Sportmedizin, Heft 1, 1985.
Liessen/Hollmann:	Ausdauersport und Stoffwechsel. Hofmann, Schorndorf 1981.
Mader, A. e.a.:	Evaluation of lactic acid anaerobic energy contribution by determination of postexercise lactic acid concentration of ear capillary blood in middle-distance runners and swimmers. Exercise Physiol. 4 (1978), 187-200.
Mattner, U.:	Lactate in Sportsmedicine. Boehringer, Mannheim 1987.
Mellerowicz:	Training – De Tijdstroom, 1977.
Nonella, L.:	Feldtest zur Ermittlung der anaeroben Schwelle. Der Läufer, 1986.
Olbrecht:	Relationship between swimming velocity and lactic concentration during continuous and intermittent training exercises. Int. J. Sports. Med. 6, 1985, p. 74-77.
Olbrecht e.a.:	De praktische betekenis van laktaatonderzoekingen voor trainingsplanning en trainingsuitvoering. Lecture at Diepenbeek on 10 November 1984.

	Publication in 'Sportmedische Tijdingen', Journal of the Flemish Union of Specialists in Sports Medicine (VVSS).
Olbrecht e.a.:	Vergleichende Untersuchungen des Laktatgeschwindigkeitsverhaltens im Zweistreckentest über 400 m Krawlschwimmen zum 30 - und 60 minutigen maximalen und 30 minutigen submaximalen Schwimmen. Deutsche Zeitschrift für Sportmedizin, Heft 1, 1985, p. 3-8.
Probst, H.:	Praktische Durchführung des Conconitests.
Riemersma, A.M.:	Fysiologische aanpassing aan grote hoogte. Sportgericht, no. 3, mei 1987.
Rispens/Lamberts:	Physiological, Biomechanical and technical Aspects of Speed Skating. Printed by: University Groningen, 1984.
Stegmann:	Bestimmung der Individuellen Schwelle bei unterschiedlich Ausdauertrainierten auf Grund des Verhaltens der Laktatkinetik während der Arbeits- und Erholungsphase. Deutsche Zeitschrift für Sportmedizin, Heft 8, 1981, p. 213-220.
von Wanner:	Subjektive Einstufung der Belastung bei Ausdauerleistungen. Deutsche Zeitschrift für Sportmedizin, Heft 4, 1985, p. 102-112.

Glossary

Acidosis:	Lactate (lactic acid) accumulation in muscle cells, causing performance level to go down.
ADP:	Adenosine diphosphate.
Aerobic-anaerobic transition:	Energy supply within this range is both aerobic and anaerobic. Production and breakdown of lactate are equal. This range is between 2 and 4 mM.
Aerobic endurance capacity:	Effort at which no lactate accumulation takes place. May be maintained long.
Aerobic energy supply:	Energy supply with sufficient oxygen. No lactate accumulation.
Aerobic threshold:	Exertion to this level takes place fully aerobic. Lactate content is about 2 mM.
Anaerobic endurance capacity:	The capacity of muscles to keep on working without sufficient oxygen intake.
Anaerobic energy supply:	Energy supply with insufficient oxygen. There is an accumulation of lactate.
Anaerobic threshold:	When performing above this level lactate accumulation takes place rapidly. Lactate content is about 4 mM.
ATP:	Adenosine triphosphate. High energy compound.
Calorie:	The quantity of heat required to heat 1 gram of water 1 degree C (kcal = 1000 cal) (1 cal = 4.18 J).
Conconi's test:	Without taking blood samples, so without lactate determination deflection pulse or deflection pace is determined. This test uses factors pulse rate and velocity.
Condition:	The sum total of physical and mental factors influencing sports performance, such as stamina, strength, speed, coordination and mental aspects.
CP:	Creatine phosphate: high-energy phosphate present in muscle cells. At maximum efforts the high-energy phosphates (ATP and CP) are exhausted after 10 to 20 seconds.
Deflection point:	The pulse rate or level of effort above which lactate accumulation takes place.
Ergometer:	Instrument measuring effort, e.g., bicycle ergometer or treadmill.
Extensive/intensive:	Two notions used in comparative sense intensive = of short duration extensive = of long duration.
Glucose:	Grape sugar, an important carbohydrate.
Glycogen:	Store of glucose, depots in liver and muscles.
L:	Lactate or lactic acid.
Lactate:	By-product (waste product) of the oxidation of glucose with insufficient oxygen.
Lactate tolerance training:	Training the lactic system. During this training high lactic values arise.

172

O_2:	Oxygen.
Phosphate battery:	Quantity of ATP and CP.
PR:	Pulse rate.
RP:	Running pace. As for the principles set forth in this book, it may be read as cycling pace, skiing pace, etc.
$\dot{V}O_2$:	Oxygen intake per minute.
$\dot{V}O_2$ max.:	Maximum oxygen intake per minute.
V:	Velocity, combined with a number (e.g., V_4), it is that speed that goes together with a lactate content of 4 mM/l. When combined with d (e.g., V_d) it is that speed at which the deflection point is.

Conversion table, measures and weights and metric system:						
1 foot	=	30.480 cm		1 cm	=	0.394 inch
1 inch	=	2.54 cm		1 meter	=	1.094 yards
1 mile	=	1609 m = 1.6 km		1 km	=	0.622 mile
1 yard	=	91.44 cm				
1 pound	=	0.454 kg		1 kg	=	2.203 pounds